SOMETHING BREWING

An Anthology from the York Pen to Paper Writers' Group

Something Brewing

An Anthology from the York

Pen to Paper Writers' Group

edited by

Lizzi Linklater

& Margaret Evans

First published in 2022 by Lendal Press
Woodend, The Crescent, Scarborough, YO11 2PW
an imprint of Valley Press · lendalpress.com

Editorial material © Lizzi Linklater 2022
Individual copyright © as credited 2022

A CIP catalogue record for this book is available from the
British Library.

ISBN 978-1-912436-86-6
Catalogue No. LP0013

Book design by Jazmine Linklater
Cover artwork & design by Roxannah Rio Linklater
(IG: @lucidlia_)

Printed and bound in Great Britain by
TJ Books Limited

Contents

Something Brewing

Foreward
Lizzi Linklater

In 2007 Pen to Paper burst onto York's literary scene. Fifteen years later we remain a strong, solid group retaining all the enthusiasm and focus that hallmarked its initiation. A lively bunch formed from poets, novelists, short story writers, life writers and scriptwriters, together we learn, listen, support one another, offer critiques of work, and, most importantly, we write. This makes for a dynamic, risk-taking environment where emphasis is consistently on gaining better mastery of the practices and theories of writing. Our monthly sessions are demanding, rewarding and fun.

Pen to Paper has not been shy in giving voice to its work, having performed at The York Literature Festival firstly in 2009 at Miller's Yard, and then in 2017 at York Theatre Royal. An anthology; something concrete to cherish and pore over, while having long been an idea on the horizon, has never quite come to fruition. All this has changed because here, in your curious grasp, you hold our literary debut.

In Something Brewing you'll find the range of writing forms that characterise the group: Poetry charting the scientific, the personal, the joyful, the topical, the ekphrastic, the spiritual, laced through with rich, relevant Japanese forms; Stories of intense contemporary realism, of tragedies executed in York, of powerful kindnesses, of entertaining wit, of delicate hope after loss, of fae-fuelled fantasy and of one deliciously subversive Bear; The everyday effects of death on a family are explored in a radio drama and a discomforting stage play twists around Russian folklore as it leads to its conclusion.

Each of these pieces has been drafted, shared, critiqued, edited and reworked. The collection comes together through sheer effort, persistence and the editorial insistence that it is as polished as it can be while encouraging the voice of the writer to be heard. Myself and Margaret (working together as editors) applaud the writers on their professionalism, good humour and patience.

Something Brewing began its life in late 2019 where we met in the Upstairs Room of the Brigantes Pub on Micklegate. Building an anthology was always going to be a lengthy project due to the sheer number of writers involved and our insistence on quality. What we did not anticipate, what no one anticipated, was the coronavirus pandemic. From early 2020 our happy gatherings abruptly ceased. With minimal fuss we signed up to Zoom, went virtual and continued the painstaking process there.

The title and image on the front cover are triple-fold alluding to the brewing of the unexpected storm of Covid -19; the frothing up of the imaginative mind as it works to produce qualitative text and a reference to Brigantes itself; a haven of restorative refreshment to assist our literary endeavours. To add to the poignancy, Brigantes Pub has gone. Another casualty of the pandemic.

Finally, the magnificent writers of Pen to Paper are the glad authors of Something Brewing and I couldn't be prouder of them. Here is something tangible, something glorious, something collaborative built through this dark period that manifests their talent, industry, loyalty and perseverance.

Lizzi Linklater

January 2022

This Glass
Joanne Foxton

All poems should be read out loud. Sometimes they need props as well.
So, stand tall, lift up your hand – preferably with a glass in it - and say:

This glass…

This glass is filled with the pale,
the gold, the amber,
the red,
the nut-brown, the bitter.
And the dark.

This glass...
is laced with foam.
Kisses from lips,
bearded faces,
sweat smeared fingers, aching from work.
And honey drenched summers.

This Glass.

This glass is loaded with friendship,

chipped with nervous laughter,
overflowing with bitter tears
and drained dry of love.
There are endless refills.

This glass...
This vessel of a thousand voices,
an oddleplex of tales
shared with friends and strangers,
or chewed over alone.
A cresting wave of life pours over the pint line.

Drink up,
Let's share another.

The Waitress
Jon Markes

She's exactly how Franky described her; tall, jet-black hair tied into a loose bun at the back. Just the right amount of lipstick. Enough mascara to elongate her eyelashes a little. Very pretty. How couldn't she be very pretty?

He's good with details is Franky, good at noticing things. In another life, he might have made a detective. Imagine that! Granted, he's not always used his skills of observation towards what most people would think of as a positive purpose, but he was always the most reliable, the most astute and that's why we used him so often.

And, it's not just the way she looks that he got right. Franky perfectly described the way she walks ('like she's gliding across the floor', he said, 'or like a swan'). Watching her move effortlessly between the tables, I can see exactly what he means.

Franky told me she gets here at a quarter to nine and leaves at five. On the dot. On the days she works, she catches the number fifty-three into town at eight-thirteen and the five-twenty home. She has a half hour break at two o'clock, once the lunchtime rush is over. Sometimes, she goes to the shops, or sits in the park to eat her lunch.

Most Thursday lunchtimes, she goes to the library. Franky thinks she must be a bit of a reader, judging by the number of books she takes out each week. He has never seen her meet anyone on the way to, or from work and that's good; the fewer people around her, the fewer the complications. Of course, she would have seen Franky when he sat in here drinking tea, but she won't have remembered him. He never spoke to her, kept his head down. He operates in the shadows, does Franky. Makes himself invisible, even when he's there.

Her boss must love her, the way she has a smile and a friendly word for every customer that comes through the door. I'll wait until she smiles and comes over to me. Then I'll make my move.

Too soon? Maybe I should come here a few times more, become a regular. I could get to know her better, win her trust. She has to trust me. She might even get to like me, want to get to know me better and that would make everything so much easier.

When I had plenty of time to imagine, I would be strolling out with her on my arm. I'd be so proud. 'Dump the old guy,' they'd say as we'd go by and she would laugh and I would pull her closer to me.

I wouldn't care.

She'd be mine.

Or else, I'd imagine us going for a nice meal. We'd have all the courses and I'd buy a bottle of expensive Italian wine. A nice Chianti, perhaps, or a Barolo if I was feeling a little more flush. She looks like she would appreciate a nice red. After the meal, we'd go to her flat for coffee. I bet it's lovely. Franky's been there already, well, outside of it and he says it's really modern, in a nice area. But that's a long way off and I should not be thinking these thoughts. Not, yet. I wonder what she reads. I asked Franky once, but he couldn't say. Of course, I shouldn't have asked him. I'm tactless, sometimes.

Surely, she could work somewhere better than this? A girl like her should be working in one of those fancy cafés, where they serve ten different kinds of coffee. Not that I've ever tasted any of them.

She's coming over. I can feel butterflies flapping away in my gut. Haven't had those for years, not since…well, a long time ago. Remember, first impressions and all that. Don't want to put her off before I've even started!

'Hi! How are you, today?' she asks. She has a beautiful smile; shiny white, perfectly straight teeth. Not too much make-up, just the lipstick and the mascara. I like that. I've never been one for women dolling themselves up.

'I'm very well thank you. How about you?' I smile back at her and clench my hands together under the table to stop them shaking.

'I'm really good, thanks. What can I get you?'

'Just a pot of tea. Thank you.' I smile again.

'Ok, it'll just be a couple of minutes,' she says. Now I've had a closer look, I would say she was handsome, rather than pretty. Too tall to be pretty.

She's having a laugh with the couple at the next table. She rests her hand on the gentleman's back as she speaks. I don't like that, but I let it go. A friendly gesture, that's all it is. She clears their table, quickly, effortlessly.

Courage.

I put my hand into the air, almost involuntarily. She comes straight over and beams that beautiful smile.

'Can I trouble you for a slice of toast?' I ask.
I'm very polite. Too polite and it sounds wrong.

'Of course,' she says.

Polite never seems genuine coming from the likes of me. It's certainly not a characteristic that anyone who knows me would recognise! Straight talking? Certainly. Loyal? Yes, regrettably. A bit of a hard man, some would say. But, polite? Hardly. But neither am I the man who stared out from the front pages of the tabloids. Nor was I ever the monster they made me out to be. I admit I wasn't right in those days, but I was not a monster. Ask those who really knew me. Ask Franky.

I'm sorted now, they say. Passed the courses, done the work, ticked the boxes. Older, wiser. Much older. But I'm actually glad they always show that picture. It's so far from how I look now it would be difficult for anyone to recognise me. She doesn't, at least I don't think she does. New life, new name.

New girl in my life. And a new man in hers, if it all turns out like I want it to.

My eyes follow her to the counter. On a sunny day, we could go to the park. Or, to the cinema, if it's raining. I wonder what kind of films she watches. Twenty-nine, she is. Twenty-third of June her birthday. What do twenty-nine-year-olds watch these days? RomComs? No, she looks too smart to watch RomComs. She's a reader, after all. Maybe an arty film. Or one of those dark Scandinavian ones that everyone seems to watch. I can't abide them myself; I end up getting angry with the stupidity of the cops. Or laughing at them.

Twenty-nine. There must be someone in her life, though Franky is sure she lives on her own. A good-looking girl like that is never on their own for long, I told him. Maybe there was someone, once. Franky did wonder how she managed to afford that flat on a waitress's wage. He said he could do a bit more digging if I wanted him to, but I made it crystal clear that I didn't want him to pry too much, other than to know where she worked and where she lived. That was the limit of his involvement and he knows better than to cross lines.

There's no ring, though. I clocked that.

She's laughing about something, with the boy behind the counter. She throws her head back. Her neck is long, slender. They look over at me and catch me looking at them. I look away. Are they laughing at me? I feel my face flush red. A dead giveaway, always. I recognise the signs and I have to be careful. Jealousy, is it? Maybe, just a tinge. Anger, is it? I hope not, for his sake. And mine.

Here she comes with the tea and toast.

'Thank you,' I say.

'You're welcome,' she says, but her smile is different this time.

'Sounded like a good joke,' I say.

'I'm sorry?' she says, frowning and taking a step back.

'Over there. When you were laughing. With the young man.'

'It was just a stupid joke,' she says.

She looks at me for quite a while. It makes me uncomfortable. I open a square of hard butter and attempt to scrape it across my toast. God, I wish I had waited now. This was not the place. She moves away.

I imagine what Franky would say: 'Too hasty, Charlie, much too hasty.'

I glance up at the counter. They're both looking at me now and she's saying something to him. He puts his hand on her shoulder. It's only a gesture on his part, but it makes my stomach churn. Not butterflies this time, not anger. Something else. Something more...protective. She tetchily brushes it off, shakes her head and turns away.

Her smile has gone.

The moment I have waited so long for has gone.

I know exactly what I have to do.

I finish my tea, fold the butter wrappers into neat little squares and put my empty mug on top of the plate. One thing I've always been is tidy.

I really don't want to leave a mess.

I go to the counter to pay.

'Thank you, that was lovely,' I say.

She gives me a quick glance and taps the amount into the till. No smile this time.

'Keep the change,' I say. At least I have been able to give her something.

'But you gave me a fifty-pound note.'

I smile at her. 'I know.'

As I open the door I turn around. She's looking straight at me.

'Goodbye.' I almost say her name. I walk out onto the street and don't look back.

I won't see her again. It's not the right thing to do. Her mother will have told her I died years ago and it's better left that way.

Gift
David Kennard

After our daughter's funeral we walked
the Brontë Trail, seeking solace
in Anne's footsteps.

We chanced on a herd of deer, fifty or more,
grazing in a field sheltered by woods.

Three fawns noticed us,
came closer.

You pulled up a handful of grass
(as if they didn't have enough)
and offered it through the wire fence.

Graciously, one came forward
to accept your consoling gift.

Moroccan Meeting
Graham Clift

That's exactly right, Tuesday, Channel 4, 8pm *Zachary Corncrake Does Africa*. Come in, come in. Fancy a journalist remembering my programme! So, you worked for the TV Times before moving to Feature Film Fortnightly? Would you like some tea?

He'll be back anytime now. Help yourself to cake. You bringing up my old programme's taking my mind back. I've been so lucky: panto; musicals; a West End trouser dropper; 15 years as Greasy Bob in Corrie; Strictly; and then the travelogue. That's where I met him. Funny, they say avoid children and animals, don't they? I had both to contend with that day. I remember it all so clearly: we were East of Rabat, a desert location on day two of filming:

* * *

'Didn't you used to be a hoofer yourself?' Darren the cameraman, said.

I said, 'Darren, show some respect for the star.' I mean, how do you get a donkey to budge if it doesn't want to?'

'Perhaps it's Method,' said Darren.

'Oh, you think he's working out his backstory, looking for the motivation?' I said. He did have that mean but slightly puzzled look of Marlon Brando.

Sunny, the director, shouted, 'Take five!' He'd had enough. And I don't just mean the tequila. They say the script editor had him up all night.

He came over, 'Zach,' he said, 'stay under your brolly love, you'll wreck the continuity if you get sunburn before Marrakesh. Now what's wrong?'

I said, 'Sunny, I'm fine, it's my co-star Marlon here, we just haven't got that chemistry. He's not for moving, does he need a carrot or something?'

'I'll get the animal wrangler,' he said.

'There's no need for THAT!' I said.

'WILLIAM WILL KNOW WHAT TO DO,' he said, dead stroppy. That's when I realised, he hadn't said *animal strangler* at all.

I blame Wendy Wardrobe. 'Ooh no,' she said, 'you can't wear hearing aids with a fez. On the backlit shots you'll look like you've got a builder's bucket on your head.'

Darren came back from getting the sand out of his lenses. 'There's a bloke looking for you,' he said, and he twitched his lips.

I'm not going to lower myself, I thought. I said, 'Are you talking to me or the donkey?' Darren just shrugged. 'Well, is he carrying a carrot?' I said.

Then I heard it.

'Hey Kellogg,' and my blood turned to ice. Use it, I said to myself. Use it to keep your cool.

The voice took me straight back to school: I'm curled up on the playground.

'Hey: Just like that. Nice fez Kellogg, I thought it were you.'

'William Warbridge, what are you doing in Morocco? I haven't seen you since you were expelled for putting mice in Frosty Fison's handbag.' He still looked and sounded the same, like a big kid.

He said, 'That weren't fair, were it? 'Ow could anyone know she was 'lergic to mouse droppin's?'

I said, 'Well, we all knew she kept Tic-Tacs loose in the bottom of her handbag. She'd slip one in between the telling-off bits in assembly.'

'I knew that, Kellogg, but who would've thought she'd actually *eat* a mouse droppin'? They don't even taste minty.'

Sunny popped up then, 'Zach, love, I see you've met Will, any rapport yet?'

'Oh aye,' said William, 'we go back a long way.'

'Marvellous', said Sunny, 'but I *meant*, with the donkey.'

'Oh yeah,' said William, 'I just came to tell him.'

'Oh. You're the animal wrangler?' I said.

'That's right,' he said.

'Well, get on with it,' said Sunny, 'we need to resume before the sandstorm arrives.'

'Righto,' said William. 'All you have to do is to speak into his left ear.'

'Left ear?'

'Aye, he's deaf in t'other.'

'What do I say?' I said.

'Dancin's shite,' he said.

'I beg your pardon, William?'

'*Dancin's shite.* It's what mi dad used to say, when he caught me dancing in mi room.'

'What?'

'When I danced, it used to make me guinea pig whistle, and that made me laugh. It was the happiest I ever was as a kid. Till he caught me. He used to tease me and bully me, shouting, 'Dancin's shite!' at me. I swore then I'd show 'im. I'd work with animals AND get into show business. Now I teach it as a command to all me animals. It like, means, Action.'

I said the words and Marlon sprang to life. Like an old stager, he looked back at me first, wiggled his ears and we stepped out like Fred and Ginger, his front legs in synchrony with mine. Such depth of character.

William said, 'E likes you, you're a natural.'

Then he took off his cap and said, 'I'm so sorry I was cruel to you when we were kids.'

That must've been tough for him to say.

I said, 'No it's alright, you were a victim yourself, you were hurt and lashing out.'

'In my experience,' he said, 'donkeys, are always right about people.'

'Perfect,' said Sunny, 'now can we roll?'

* * *

The three of us: William, Marlon and me, have been the best of friends ever since. Soon after, William's star rose. He was wrangler for the *Lassie* remake (twenty dogs!), and then *Zombie Goldilocks*. After *Revenge of All Creatures Great and Small* he never looked back. We moved in together after my travelogue bombed, and now I stay home to look after all the animals.

Just a minute that's a message on my phone. It's Will. Oh dear, I'm sorry, he's got to fly out to Hollywood this afternoon, can he re-arrange? Problems with *Dumbo and the Mutants III*, apparently.

Three Blind Mice: A Stage Play
Loreta Vilkyte

CHARACTERS
MIKE: A middle-aged man, English
LIANA: Mike's wife middle-aged woman, Russian
TOMAS: Their son aged 5 (Little Tomas)
TOMAS: The same son aged 15, a boarder at a
private school

ACT I   SCENE 1
>   **TOMAS (15)** IN THE BOARDING
>   SCHOOL'S YARD. HE LOOKS
>   IRRITATED. HIS DAD IS LATE.

TOMAS (15-YEAR-OLD): (LOOKS AT HIS WATCH)
        Where is he? (TO HIMSELF) Don't
        panic, don't, please don't, don't...
        (DESPERATE) Where is he? Always late
        to collect me from school. Always.
        Yes, he's right. I'm a boarder and
        'boarders are bored...'Shit… I can't
        wait this long... I'll have a panic
        attack! Shit… where is he?(BREATHING
        HEAVILY) Right... (HE GRABS A BEER
        BOTTLE FROM HIS SCHOOL BAG AND
        STARTS SPEAKING TO THE AUDIENCE)
        I was five years old. We lived in
        Russia...

>   **MIKE** AND **LIANA** APPEAR IN FRONT
>   OF HIM. SPOTLIGHT ON THEM

>   SITTING AT THE TABLE WITH
>   A STORY BOOK, A CAKE AND A
>   KITCHEN KNIFE ON IT. THERE IS
>   AN EMPTY CHAIR BETWEEN THEM
>   IN THE MIDDLE. THERE IS A
>   DUSTER NEXT TO THE TABLE AND
>   A PLASTIC BAG CONTAINING A
>   SMARTPHONE, A ROPE, A BROCHURE
>   AND SOME CRISPS.

MIKE: (TEACHES **LIANA** CORRECT PRONUNCIATION)
            Three, say *three* not tree. Try
            again, tongue between your teeth.
            Three,
            three...

LIANA: Th...ree. Three!

MIKE: Correct. Three blind mice, three
            blind mice. See how they run, see
            how they run. Say it.

LIANA: Tree blind mice, (LAUGHS) sorry,
            three blind mice…
            I've had enough.

MIKE: Once more.

LIANA: No.

MIKE: You're nearly there...

LIANA: No.

MIKE: If you practise...

LIANA: No.

MIKE: ...no one will ever notice that you
            are a foreigner when we're back in
            Britain.

LIANA: No!

MIKE: Your son speaks better English than
            you, Liana.

LIANA: Yes, because I taught him!

>   THEY TURN THEIR BACKS TO EACH
>   OTHER. **LITTLE TOMAS** RUNS IN
>   WITH HIS SHREK TOY IN HIS
>   HANDS AND SITS BETWEEN HIS
>   PARENTS.

TOMAS: Story time, Mum...

LIANA: (TAKES A BOOK) Yes...where were we?(READS) "...Cracking twigs, branches catching in your hair, creeping tendrils of mist swirling around your ankles."

MIKE: Typical. Russians. They can scare you to death even with their fairy tales.

LIANA: "This wasn't just any birch forest, for in this forest lived the terrifying witch called Baba-Yaga. A bony-legged witch, who ate people like others ate chicken."

MIKE: I don't think this story is for children.

LIANA: (WITH DETERMINATION TO READ FURTHER) We love chicken, don't we? (SHE KISSES **TOMAS)**.

TOMAS: Shrek likes it too.

LIANA: (READS FURTHER ON) "A fence made of human bones Surrounded Baba-Yaga's hut and the roof was crowned with human skulls."

MIKE: Can you put that book away please?

LIANA: Khorosho, right, good. I'll read it in Russian because everything sounds scarier in English.

MIKE: Stop it, Liana. You know that he'll have to be fluent IN ENGLISH when we live in Britain. (TO **TOMAS**) Bedtime sweetie.

TOMAS: Oh...

LIANA: Spat, spat, spat, sleep, sleep, sleep...

TOMAS: Shrek doesn't want to sleep...

MIKE: Yes, he does.

TOMAS: Oh... (WALKS AWAY).

MIKE: Listen. I work all day. I pay the bills. I take good care of Tomas.

LIANA: What does that have to do with fairy

tales?

MIKE: I'll tell you what. I'm fed
            up living in a country full of
            horror stories and...and misshapen
            perfectionism. Seeing all these
            corrupt oligarchs being adored by
            peasants makes me sick. Sick! We're
            going back to Britain.

LIANA: But people voted for Brexit! We
            won't feel welcome.

MIKE: Britain has the fifth largest economy
            in the world. The future is there,
            Liana.

LIANA: Why did you vote out then if you
            already had it all?

MIKE: Listen to me, please. Why do you
            think foreigners are swamping
            British schools with their offspring?
            Why? Education my dear! Our boarding
            schools provide...

LIANA: We are not going.

MIKE: We? Who is 'we'?

LIANA: Tomas and I. (STARTS CUTTING THE
            CAKE) Cake?

MIKE: Listen. You can probably get a top
            job in a University with all the
            languages you speak.

LIANA: (STARTS EATING THE CAKE) I'm not
            sure if I can cope alongside all the
            cooking...

MIKE: Spaghetti and Aldi sauce?

LIANA: Cleaning?

MIKE: A monkey can clean, Liana!

LIANA: Pardon?

MIKE: Come on. Nobody is going to pay you
            for looking after your own family.

LIANA: Eat your cake.

MIKE: I said no. (PAUSE) Are you going to
            that lecture I told you about? The
            Christine Armstrong one?

LIANA: (SHRUGS)

MIKE: (SNEERY) You know, 'The Mother of All
          Jobs?' She wrote that manifesto for
          families. 'How to Work and Be Happy
          with Children?'
LIANA: No.
MIKE: No?
LIANA: No.

          LIANA AND **MIKE** FREEZE.
          SPOTLIGHT ON **15-YEAR OLD**
          TOMAS.

TOMAS: That's how everything started. With
          the fairy tales... like dark forests
          and branches catching your hair...
          Still, I was a happy boy who loved
          his Mummy and Daddy...
          (WATCHES THE FOLLOWING SCENE).

          LITTLE TOMAS RUNS IN AND PUTS
          HIMSELF BETWEEN HIS PARENTS
          AND STARTS PLAYING ON AN
          IMAGINARY X-BOX.

TOMAS: Watch me kill!
LIANA: Switch it off Tomas.
MIKE: You can play a bit longer...
LIANA: (DEEP BREATH IN) Would you like to go
          to the beach Tomas?
TOMAS: (PLAYING) Watch! Oh no... I am dead
          (TO **MIKE**) Beach, Daddy! Would you
          like to come with us?
MIKE: What do you mean *us* sweetie?
TOMAS: Me and Mummy?
MIKE: We don't have the money for all of
          us to go.
TOMAS: You have the money, Daddy. You
          always have money.
MIKE: Alright, alright.
TOMAS: Yes. Yes. Beach!
MIKE: I've got a plan. What about if *we* -

                  me and you, go to the beach instead?
                  (HUGS HIM). What do you think?

TOMAS: I want Mummy to come.

MIKE: I just told you, it's too expensive
                  for all of us. Put on your shoes.

                  LIANA STARTS DUSTING
                  EXCESSIVELY

LIANA: (AGGRESSIVELY) Brilliant. I'll just
                  stay here cleaning then, shall I?
                  (SHOUTING) Shall I?

                  MIKE TAKES CAR KEYS FROM HIS
                  POCKET AND A PLASTIC BAG FROM
                  THE FLOOR.

MIKE: (TO **TOMAS**) Tell me sweetie, who do
                  you love more?
                  Mummy or Daddy?

LIANA: Mike! (TO **TOMAS**) Don't forget your
                  Shrek, my prince.

TOMAS: (TO HIS TOY) Shrek, who do you love
                  more, Mummy or Daddy?

MIKE: Never mind. Let's go, son. Three
                  Blind Mice?

TOMAS: Yes. Me first Daddy.

                  THEY BOTH SIT IN AN IMAGINARY
                  CAR. **MIKE** STARTS ENGINE. THEY
                  LEAVE SINGING THREE BLIND
                  MICE.

SCENE 2

                  DAYLIGHT BECOMES DIM. **MIKE** AND
                  TOMAS APPEAR IN THE FOREST.
                  MIKE TAKES THE BROCHURE OUT OF
                  THE BAG.

TOMAS: It's a forest, Daddy.

MIKE: I know.
TOMAS: (POINTS) We saw a deer over there
           with Mummy.

           MIKE TURNS HIM AROUND TO
           ANOTHER DIRECTION AND TAKES
           OUT THE PHONE.

MIKE: This way. I've got a surprise for
           you.
TOMAS: A phone? (MIKE GIVES HIM THE PHONE)
           Thank you, Daddy.
MIKE: You can't get a signal in a real
           forest.
TOMAS: (EXPLORING HIS PRESENT) I can take
           pictures.
MIKE: Listen. I have a plan for how to
           make Mummy happy.

           MIKE LOOKS AT THE BROCHURE.
           LITTLE TOMAS AT HIS PHONE.
           SPOTLIGHT ON TOMAS (15-YEAR-
           OLD).

TOMAS(15-YEAR-OLD): That's what he said and
           I couldn't agree more. Dad was ready
           to fix everything, even my mum. I
           swear he could do this directly from
           the forest! And if Baba-Yaga was
           crunching someone's bones somewhere
           nearby, I truly believed he would
           have put her to rest.
MIKE: (LOOKING AT THE BROCHURE) This forest
           was bombarded by Germans. Did you
           know that?
TOMAS: Any werewolves Daddy?
MIKE: They exist only in fairy tales.
TOMAS: Oh...
MIKE: (POINTS) There was an airfield,
           somewhere over there... (READS)
           "They trained pilots to fly to

                    bombing missions all over Europe..."
                    This is cool Tomas. "Today, the old
                    runway areas provide home to forest
                    wildlife."
TOMAS: (SCREAMS) Wolf! Daddy! Wolf over
                    there!
MIKE: No! Don't be silly! Let's look
                    at the Bomb Storage now. This way
                    sweetie, I don't think anybody your
                    age has ever dared to go inside...
TOMAS: Really?
MIKE: (PUTS HIS HANDS ON HIS SHOULDERS) You
                    will be the First to do so, sweetie…

                    MIKE AND **LITTLE TOMAS** FREEZE.
                    SPOTLIGHT ON **TOMAS (15)**.

TOMAS (15-YEAR-OLD): Just like that. You
                    will be the first ever to stay in
                    a Baba-Yaga 's bomb storage...The
                    trees creaked and the dead leaves
                    crunched, "It's not easy to get away
                    from me, the witch snarled..."

                    MIKE TAKES A ROPE FROM HIS
                    PLASTIC BAG AND STARTS PUTTING
                    AROUND **LITTLE TOMAS'** ANKLE.
                    TOMAS (15) TAKES ANOTHER BEER
                    BOTTLE FROM HIS BAG AND STARTS
                    DRINKING.

MIKE: (TO **LITTLE TOMAS**) Stay still now
                    while I do this.
TOMAS: I am, Daddy.
TOMAS (15-YEAR-OLD): From that moment. All I
                    could think about was *the* Baba-Yaga,
                    "Stay with me. If you work well,
                    I'll keep you alive, if you don't,
                    I will cook and eat you". I said to
                    myself, Daddy can't eat me, daddies
                    simply don't eat their children.

Children are not food and I am not
a chicken. It's not how the world
works. (TO **LITTLE TOMAS**) It's not
fair... I know, it's not fair... (HE
CRIES)

MIKE IS TIGHTENING A ROPE.

TOMAS: (TO HIS TOY SHREK) What do I do
Shrek? What do I do?
MIKE: I said, stay still.
TOMAS: (HE TRIES TO PLEASE **MIKE**) Mummy
couldn't catch a pipit… could she?
MIKE: No way...
TOMAS: Mummy is too clumsy.
MIKE: She is... I have to go now.
TOMAS: I love you more than Mummy, Daddy.
MIKE: I know.
TOMAS: She left car keys in a trolley...
MIKE: That's correct. All these things
make Mummy unhappy. She needs to sit
down and think how to help herself.
And you're a big boy now. You don't
need her to be around you all the
time. Do you?
TOMAS: Shrek loves you too, Daddy...
MIKE: Listen. The rope. It's a forest.
You could get lost. Don't worry - It
won't hurt. (KEEPS TIGHTENING ROPE
If you're tied to the tree you can
explore the forest and return here
easily, safely. I will be back soon.
TOMAS: (STARTS CRYING) I don't like fairy
tales.
MIKE: Nobody does. (HE GIVES **TOMAS** CRISPS
FROM THE BAG).
MIKE: You can eat them all. I'm going now.
TOMAS: Is Mummy cooking tonight?
MIKE: Does it matter?
TOMAS: I'm not hungry!
MIKE: You know I love you. Don't you?

TOMAS: Yes…
MIKE: (WANTS TO CHEER HIS SON UP BY
SINGING): Three blind mice, three
blind mice. See how they run, see
how they run...They all run after
the farmer's wife, who cut off their
tails with a carving knife...Did
you ever see such a thing in your
life...as three blind mice...
(HE LEAVES)

LITTLE TOMAS STARTS EATING
CRISPS. TOMAS(15) SITS DOWN
NEXT TO HIM. THEY WATCH THE
FOLLOWING SCENE TOGETHER.

SCENE 3

BACK HOME. DAYLIGHT IS BRIGHT
AGAIN. MIKE CUDDLES LIANA FROM
BEHIND.

LIANA: You're back early.
MIKE (FIRMLY): I can't stay in this
country anymore. Will you come with
me?
LIANA: Not again please. (SHOUTS): Tomas,
pancakes are ready!
MIKE: I hate my job. I don't belong here.
We must leave.
LIANA: Where is Tomas?
MIKE: For God's sake! Say yes!
LIANA: Where is he?
MIKE: We are talking about *us* now, not
him.
LIANA: Did you go to the beach?
MIKE: Did you look for jobs in Britain as
I told you?
LIANA: I didn't have time.
MIKE: You can do it now.
LIANA: Pardon?

MIKE:	Show me the jobs you applied for today! Now!
LIANA	(TERRIFIED): Oh God... God... What have you done? Where is Tomas?
MIKE:	He's not with you anymore. Is he, huh?
LIANA:	Please, I'll do anything Mike!
MIKE:	Liar!
LIANA:	Anything, I swear, Mike, anything!
MIKE:	He's at the bomb storage… tied to an oak...
LIANA:	I'm calling the police!
MIKE:	You don't get it! Do you? Do you? Do you?

> **MIKE** GRABS **LIANA** BY HER NECK. **TOMAS (15)** COVERS **LITTLE TOMAS'** EYES WITH HIS HANDS. **LIANA** SCREAMS, WALKS BACKWARDS, GRABS A KNIFE. THEY BOTH FREEZE AS **LIANA** STABS **MIKE**.

> SPOTLIGHT ON **TOMAS (15)**.

TOMAS (15-YEAR-OLD): Yep, my mum stabbed my dad while I was eating crisps in Baba-Yaga's forest! He survived. Mum? She was locked up...She's still there. We don't see her. It's too expensive...Me? I woke up in a country I should belong to, Dad says, in Britain. *'Baba-Yaga won't gobble you — we left her behind'*, Dad is convinced...

> **CURTAIN**

Online source Vasilisa the Beautiful was used:
http://home.freeuk.com/russia2

26

Senryu
Jools Lambert

left on the table
a goodbye letter-
unexpected

between snow
and the homeless man…
two sheets of cardboard

ghostly ducks
fly on forever …
derelict house

a gift of time -
on the doormat
snail mail

with the passing years
harder to cut it
sweet potato

strangely erotic,
your gentle dabs of calamine
on my sunburnt neck

shoulder to wrist,
inks of time
chart her life

race day -
hats and people
worse for wear

Green Fingers (Give and It Will Be Given Unto You)
Margaret Evans

Knees creaking, Nancy sat back gratefully in the pew, her private prayer completed after the end of the service. She inhaled deeply and enjoyed the scent of freesias from the nearby flower arrangement as Steve approached.

He handed her a mug, ensuring she had a secure hold before he released his grasp. 'Weak and milky. I thought I'd save you a wait in the queue.'

'You know me so well, thank you.' She sniffed at the aromatic coffee then nodded firmly at the space next to her. All her experience as an English teacher meant she retained the air of command. Even after ten years of retirement.

Steve sank down and sipped his tea.

'So, how may I help you?' asked Nancy.

Steve raised a questioning eyebrow.

'You forget how well I can read you,' Nancy responded.

'I thought you could read minds when you taught me.'

Steve blew on his drink's surface, evidently pondering where to begin. 'What did you think of Mike's sermon?'

'I assume this is heading somewhere.' Nancy wasn't keen to admit to dozing off: eyes closed due to the sun streaming through the stained-glass window, of course.

Steve cleared his throat. 'It was about caring for others. "Give and it will be given unto you."'

'So, how can I help?'

'It's nearly work experience time for Year 10, and there's a lad in my form who hasn't found a placement yet. He's not a bad kid, but he's struggling with dyslexia so academic work's a chore, and he isn't sporty or musical, and his home life's not easy...'

'I get the picture.'

When Nancy hesitated, Steve added, 'It's only for two weeks.'

'But what kind of work can I offer him?'

'Well, since... your Bill passed away, and I've not been able to call around as much recently, and your arthritis has...er... I thought he could help in the garden instead of me. And you could teach him about plants, you've got such green fingers...'

'They might have been green once.' Nancy laughed. 'More like blue with stiffness now!'

Steve looked down; cheeks flushed.

'Sorry to tease you, Steve, you're a good friend. And I appreciate your past help: you don't have time now with the new baby. I'll do it. What's the boy's name?'

*   *   *

Josh perches on the low wall of the old biddy's home. Time for a last fag before he has to introduce himself. Narrowing his eyes against the smoke he peers at the front garden.

He doesn't have a clue about plants. The back yard at home is a place to have barbecues and lounge around in the sun with a few beers, the front door opening straight out onto the pavement. Still being here has to be better than the alternative: stuck in school.

A curtain twitch at the window catches his eye. He stubs out his roll-up under his tatty trainer, and hands stuffed in the pockets of his low-slung stressed jeans he walks up the mossy path. The door is pulled open before he has a chance to ring the doorbell, leaving him feeling a fool with his arm up in the air.

'You Mrs Sullivan?'

'Yes, and you must be Josh.' She smiles and holds out her hand. 'It's a pleasure to meet you. Do come in.'

He can't remember the last time someone shook his hand. In fact, it's been ages since he's felt anyone's touch. Her skin is warm, her fingers knobbly and twisted.

'Come into the kitchen. We'll have a drink and a chat before we start.'

She leads him down the dark hallway and settles him at the table. 'If you want a cold drink, regrettably I can offer only milk or tap water. But I have tea, coffee and drinking chocolate if you'd rather have hot?'

Josh's stomach rumbles: no breakfast. They'd run out of bread and cereal at home. 'Hot chocolate please.' It'd be the most filling.

The old woman shuffles from cupboard to kettle to cutlery drawer. Wrestling with the lid to the cocoa tin, she eventually gives up and hands it to him. 'Would you mind, please? I'm not as nimble as I once was.'

He flips it open readily and gets up to pass everything back to her.

'While you're on your feet, would you mind getting that tin down for me please?' She points at a shelf.

The container rattles promisingly as he puts it down, the top slipping off to reveal biscuits. They look home-baked, not Lidl's cheapest.

'Help yourself,' she says putting the hot drinks down with a trembly hand and waving at the food.

He's on the fourth biscuit, hot chocolate gulped down in double-quick time, before realising nothing's been said for a couple of minutes. The old woman is looking at him thoughtfully, somehow knowing what he's about. He shifts uncomfortably under her gaze.

'They're very moreish, aren't they?' she says. 'Do have another. I loved to bake but had to take a break when my arthritis worsened. Fortunately, my son recently bought me a wonder-ful food processor which does the work for me. Though it's really a guilt gift.'

'What's a guilt gift?' Josh asks, spraying crumbs out of his mouth.

'He emigrated to Australia many years ago and rarely comes back, so he plies me with expensive presents to make up for it.'

Josh nods his understanding, leans back in his chair, chewing the last mouthful of his fifth biscuit. It's the fullest his stomach has felt in ages.

'Have you had enough to eat for now?'

He nods again.

'A man of few words, I see. Well, let's get to work in the back garden.'

Nancy starts him off with easy tasks: mowing the lawn, tidying the edges, cutting back the overgrown bushes and hedge; the jobs that won't ruin her more precious plants.

In the balmy weather of the next fortnight, she sits in a deck chair, which Josh has opened out for her, and she directs his efforts, ensuring that only weeds are removed from the beds, and invisible bulbs aren't disturbed from their rest. He waters the thirsty garden, spraying himself to cool off, and eventually relaxes enough in her company to throw a few drops in her direction. It was on that day that she asked him to call her Nancy instead of Mrs Sullivan.

Mindful of his skinny frame, she feeds him bacon sandwiches for breakfast and snacks during the day, with generous lunches, sometimes with produce from the garden, once he has cleared up the vegetable patch.

They visit the garden centre for bedding plants and hanging baskets; they pore over her gardening books and surf the 'net. The resentful youth with the sullen expression and initial vocabulary of a few grunts morphs into a willing character who shows a flair for gardening. Though Nancy has had to overlook some choice language, for example when Josh dropped a heavy planter on his toe; and she's ignored the residual sweet smell of something he definitely shouldn't have been smoking.

When Steve visits to check all is well, Josh proudly shows him around, remembering the names of all the plants and their needs. Nancy knows she will be writing a glowing report about his work experience.

On the last day, both Nancy and Josh are subdued. As if reflecting their mood, the storm clouds gather.

'You'd better get inside,' says Josh.

'You too,' adds Nancy. 'You've done enough.'

'I'll just put the grass cuttings into the bags and tidy away the tools.'

Nancy is reading at the kitchen table, refreshments prepared for when Josh has finished, when the first flash of lightning illuminates the room. Thunder follows quickly on its heels, the crash making her jump. The gentle pitter-patter of raindrops against the windows becomes the insistent clatter of machine-gun fire. Torrents of water stream down the glass.

She opens the back door and tries to locate Josh in the downpour. A figure dashes towards her, and squelches inside.

'Oh dear, Josh! You're a drowned rat!'

Water drips from the ends of his long, straggly hair forming a pool at his soggy feet.

'Don't move: I'll get some towels.' Nancy climbs the stairs as quickly as she can and returns with fluffy bath sheets. 'Get the worst off, then we'll find you something dry to wear.'

Nancy's ok as adults go, thinks Josh, one of the best really, though he knows she doesn't like him smoking and swearing; that's when she squashes her lips together.

She lets him have some of her son's clothes; says he left them for when he visited from Australia, but he's too fat for them now. They're a bit short and old-fashioned but the shoes fit, and when Josh sees himself in the mirror, he feels pretty good.

'They suit you better than my son,' she says, once he's back downstairs. 'Now, let's warm you up.'

It's while they're drinking his favourite hot chocolate, that Nancy brings something up that Josh has been hoping for.

'You've done such a great job, I wondered... Would you like to carry on doing some gardening for me? At weekends maybe? I'd pay you of course.'

Josh grins so widely, he feels like his face is going to split. Christmas has come early.

By the time they actually get to Christmas, Josh has celebrated his sixteenth birthday in October, Nancy, another of hers (age undisclosed to Josh), in November, and the amount of gardening work has dribbled away to nothing. Nancy is so keen for Josh's company and to give him opportunities to earn money that she makes up requirements for decorating rooms that don't really need it, shelves that don't need putting up, light fittings that don't need changing.

Josh usually glows when he's with her, chatting away, sharing details of his life: about his mother, whom he loves, his step-father for whom he cannot say the same; friends at school, noticeably mentioning one more than others: Sophie. Nancy can hardly believe this is the same sullen, monosyllabic youth she met several months ago. But today, when she opens the door to him, his mouth is curved down, the opposite of his usual expression.

Nancy sits him down at the kitchen table. He refuses her offers of refreshment.

'What's wrong?' she asks.

'They've been talking a lot about careers at school.'

'What's the problem with that?'

'I'd like to study horticulture. But I'll never get the grades even to get to college. I'm so dyslexic.' His shoulders droop and he hangs his head.

'Don't you get help with that at school?'

'A bit but not enough. You can get extra time with exams and stuff, or even someone to read for you, but I froze up when I tried that.'

'I'm sure we can sort something out,' Nancy comforts him before setting him off to hang pictures up.

After he's gone, she turns on the computer and searches for up-to-date information about dyslexia. A few days later, she has acquired materials to help him. They spend some time in study each weekend, but progress is slow.

It's a freezing cold night in early February, and Nancy is about to go to bed when there's a knock at the door. She opens it tentatively, the chain allowing only a few inches leeway, revealing a shivering Josh. She draws him in, concern intensifying as she notices his black eye and reddening cheek. Later, drinking the inevitable hot chocolate, words tumble from his mouth.

'It's all his fault, that bastard. Things were ok with me and Mum until he turned up. Now I've been chucked out. I wouldn't have come here but I've got nowhere else to go.'

'Of course, you can stay.' Nancy recalls the weather forecast predicting temperatures well below freezing. 'But you must let your mother know you're safe.'

'I've slept rough before and she's been ok.'

'Still, I'd be happier if she knew.'

Josh leaves a voicemail and a text, as there's no reply to his attempts to call.

The next morning, Josh manages to get through. Nancy hears only one side of the conversation, but it doesn't sound good. She holds out her hand for the mobile: 'May I speak with her please?'

Josh shrugs and passes it over.

'Hello Mrs Shriver. I wondered whether I could offer at least a temporary solution. I have a spare bedroom which Josh could use, at least until matters calm down. Would that suit?'

Nancy tilts her head at Josh seeking approval. He nods enthusiastically. There is agreement at the other end of the call too.

Temporary stretches into long term. Josh meets with his mum, but in a café or, when the weather becomes more welcoming, in the park.

Nancy no longer makes up tasks for Josh to complete. Instead, they have the opportunity for more intensive study interspersed with school, the occasional gardening and hot chocolate. And dates with Sophie. Josh makes good progress: by exam time he has gained confidence, Nancy has enjoyed his success and the opportunity to flex her teaching muscles again.

Come August, Nancy is the first person he phones about his results.

'I've got the grades, Nancy! I'll get to study horticulture.'

'That's great news. I'm so pleased for you.'

'Couldn't have done it without you. Thank you so much.'

Nancy hears whooping in the background.

'That's Sophie. She's going to college too. Got to go.'

Nancy puts the phone down, a smile playing around her mouth. Give and it will be given unto you.

Haiku
Jools Lambert

a lone goose
honks its way
across dark roof tops

orange-pink hues
a summer palette
for twilight

an empty field
only ravens disturb
the fallow time

from the birchwood-
my silent watchfulness
returned

a seal's plaintive call
breaks my reverie
Dublin bay farewell

disturbed by moonlight
across the darkness
geese call

an abandoned slag heap
its own eco-system-
brambles and birds

travelling slowly across
the bay's inky dark
a Blackberry moon

Final Exit
Tina Anderson

Why did I drag you into the cellar? Of course, I know why, but I don't want to say. It's a sin. Even though you were only a Jewess. But you didn't say anything. So maybe it was all right. No, it wasn't alright. I saw in your eyes, the terror, the hate. But I could not stop myself. I've never done it before though I know other priests do. I've only thought about it. But there you were, running for your life, then you tripped right outside on my doorstep. Your tiny waist was just like a child's so I put my hands round you and just slid you inside. I was shaking and my hands left two sweaty marks on your dress but no-one else noticed in all the smoke, the drumming and the chanting; First we'll kill the Jews and then we'll kill the infidels. Malebisse and his men whipping up the crowd - setting fires all over the city in their Crusading madness. The crowd would have killed you. Don't stare at me like that. Why don't you speak? What am I going to do with you?

*

What's he thinking? What else is he going to do with me? It couldn't be any worse than what he's done. His thing, his hairiness, His scrabbling fingers. Can I even get up and walk? I'm sure there's a gaping hole from there right up into my chest. But I'm not going to just lay here and die. I've got to think. Not about what's happened. It's too late for that. I can't run away. I'll have to stay. I'll have to speak to him. Not yet though. I'll just rest here. If I open my mouth now, I will surely be sick. I won't be sick in front of him. He's getting down on his knees. He's praying, fiddling with his beads. Well, I can pray too. *Remember Miriam, you are a Rabbi's daughter*, my father's always telling me. I squeeze my eyes shut and force the breath from my mouth, *Shema Yisrael Adonai Eloheinu Adonai Ehad* – Hear, O Israel, the Lord is our God, the Lord is One. Stop it! Shut up, shut up he's shouting at me now, but I lift up my head and continue without faltering, the strength seeping back into my bones. I remember Rabbi Akiva who endured his flesh being torn with iron combs and died reciting the Shema. They say he pronounced the last word with his last breath. *Never underestimate the power of prayer, Miriam.* Yes, prayer is power, I know that now. But I'm not Rabbi Akiva and I'm not going to die. Not yet.

*

I need to think about what to do with you because it's growing dark. I'm going to go outside and I know you won't run away, because you've got nowhere to go and no-one to help you. The street is empty, everyone must be at the castle shouting at the Jews. They must have shut themselves away inside. Torches are burning and the siege engines have been dragged into place, casting monstrous shadows. The Jews are throwing stones down onto the crowd. One of those crazed itinerant monks who believe their purpose is to rant and rave up and down the country is standing halfway up the mound and shouting about the crucifixion when the Jews murdered Jesus. It's surely a view of hell._

*

What is he doing? I'm going to see. He's standing in the street staring at the Castle. Flames are shooting up into the night sky. The fire roars like a living beast, thick smoke blackening the red glow. Suddenly the crowd is silent. There is a curious smell like candles - not the fine beeswax candles my mother always buys - more like the cheap tallow ones they burn in shops. And the smell of roasting meat. I can't breathe and I have to grab hold of him to stay on my feet and I call out to my mother and father but they are not there. They must be in the smoke rising up and I shout and scream so my breath follows them up into the blackness.

*

Shut up, I'm going put you back in the cellar and gag you for your own good. Now you've bitten me like the rabid little bitch you are. Someone might come, then I'll be in trouble for harbouring a Jewess. What are you doing, rocking back and forth your eyes rolling like a cow in the shambles? You've soaked the gag with spittle and your dress has ridden up and there's blood and slime on your legs. You are like some fantastic gargoyle, you are not human, you disgust me. If I take off the gag, will you scream again? You shake your head. You lay prostate like a novice nun trembling through the fine fabric of your dress, I can see your arched backbone, your thin wrists and your heavy gold bracelets rattling on the floor. What can I do? Who can help me? Oh Lord, who can help me? I can't move or breathe; my lungs are solid lobes of stone.

*

He's babbling away I must think, no not about that. No, about what to do. I force myself onto my knees. Stop gibbering, I tell him, and fetch Agnes the wool merchant's daughter. She won't be down at the castle watching the Jews burn. She will help me. I want Agnes. Please, I beg you go and find her. She's my friend, she doesn't care that I'm Jewish. She will help me. I know she will help me.

*

What, you expect me to go out and bring back the wool merchant's daughter? The wool merchant is built like a bull. They say he still worships the old gods up there on the moors, when he goes to buy his fleeces. He's a heathen with no respect for the holy church. What if he sees me? And what can this girl, this Agnes do? I won't go, so shut up and let me think.

*

He's shaking like the milksop he is. I must stiffen his resolve. I tell him the wool merchant is away. There's only Agnes at home, looking after her brothers. And you can be sure they'll be down at the castle jumping up and down shouting about Jews drinking blood and eating poor Christian babies. Go or I will go myself. If you want rid of me, go.

*

What have I done – it was your fault, filthy whore, you led me astray, I could kill you but how? By smothering you or cutting your throat or throwing you in the river? No, I can't do that. Not that. Then I'll really burn in hell unless I buy a cartload of indulgences and why am I talking to you out loud? You are laughing like a crone and I can see your small pointy teeth. Your indulgences are fakes you say. All made from driftwood. For your sins you will need the thighbone of your Jesus himself for your salvation. The thighbone of a Jew you say. I can't think, my head is throbbing. So, I will go yes, outside, away from you. I'll fetch this Agnes. Anything to get you out of here.

*

He's gone. I stand up and walk stiffly round and round the cellar. I don't want to pray any more. I don't want to die muttering the Shema. I want to shout at God. I often want to shout at God and my father says, *Miriam, remember Job, you were born with nothing, and you will surely die with nothing. The Lord gave and now he* has taken away. May his name be praised! Well, good for Job. I'm not Job. I'm me and I want to live.

*

It's strangely quiet in the street. I can't stop my shaking and I walk touching the wall until I find the fine door to the wool merchant's house. The brass knocker, shaped as a ram, is so heavy I can hardly raise it. The door opens and a girl as tall as a man stands there. Miriam the Jewess sent me; I tell her. She needs help. I've saved her from the crowds but she needs to leave. She needs to go, she can't stay in my house, not a minute longer.

*

He's come back with Agnes. She's brought boy's clothes and I strip and put them on. She raises her hand to her mouth, then turns to face the priest and her hand snakes out and she grabs him between his legs. I see the bulging muscles in her arm, strong like a boy's and her pale skin covered in fine gold down and then he's on the floor gasping like a carp out of water. Be careful, she warns him or I'll tell my brothers it was me you defiled not her. They will cut you up and feed you to the swine. She looks at me. Well, Miriam, the boy's clothes suit you. My father has a boat on the staithe ready to sail with the tide and you must leave with it. The holy man will kindly escort us. These clothes are itchy, I say, and she slaps me. Just shut up, she hisses and do what I say.

*

People are now running away from the castle but the muscular Agnes shoves me forward and I try to force my way against the throng of people. They see my priest's black cassock and most step aside and you both follow docile as you like but I know the ginger one has a knife and she'll cut off my genitals if she has to._

*

I get in the boat and lie on the bales of wool under a canopy made of stretched hide. The boat master is coming back, a man even darker skinned than me. He jumps lightly onto the deck. You will take this boy and deliver him to the nearest community of Jews outside England, Agnes tells him. I lift the hide and look. Will he take me? His eyes flicker and she shoves a purse into his hand. The boat is rocking gently but the man says nothing. People are now gathering on the staithe and talking with the priest and pointing but mercifully the boat swings away from the berth.

I peer out again from under the stinking hide and see Agnes still on the landing and we both know we will never meet again, in this world or any other. Her hair glows like the halo Christians paint round the heads of their saints. Now the cold river flushes me downstream away from this city of death. Yet I can't stop whimpering; I want to go home; I want to go home. The boatman bends down and hands me a flagon filled with water. You have no home, he says. No home to go to.

Absence of Jews
Through hatred, or indifference,
A gap they slip through, a conscience
That corrodes more deeply since it is
Forgotten – that deadens York.

(From 'Astringencies – The Coldness' from The Complete Poems of Jon Silkin. Ed. by Jon Glover & Kathryn Jenner published by Carcanet)

Hurrah for the Black-Browed Babbler!
Martin Watts

...BLACK BROWED BABBLER BIRD STOP FOUND STOP
BORNEO STOP...REUTERS

They've found the Black-Browed Babbler!
It's been lost for a hundred years.
They found it deep in the forest.
It seems, it just re-appears.

They searched high and low, in Borneo,
'We're sure,' they announced, 'it's extinct'.
But the Babbler smiled, still free and wild,
sat on his twig, and winked.

He looks like a writer in trouble,
a poet all cross and perplexed,
squinting and frowning, glaring and scowling,
missing his reading specs.

Let's hope for the sake of the Babbler,
his worries will soon all be gone.
With his inky black eye, he'll play, 'I spy'
and babble his favourite song.

12.03.21

A Wish to Lie
Joanne Foxton

I've been a long time coming home.

The Forge and Farrier Inn still sits at the turn in the road, fat with rooms to rent and places to drink, and last night I remembered how to move to the dance of the bartender as I served old friends and new with beer and laughter. But it is not my home. Established nearly 400 years, this ugly toad of a stone dwelling filled with iron that burns my skin and drains my magic, squats at the bottom of a wooded hill where the spring that I sprang from flows, and a stone, gifted by people from a dark age who both worshipped and bound me here, stands. Threaded through its foundations are ink-written chains of knowledge and ownership that bind me as much as they describe me. I am the ghost in the mist, the last wish on the first star of evening, the monster under the bed. I am Todd, named after the foxglove that still grows in the woods beyond. I am fae, and this is my homecoming.

The back kitchen of the Forge holds that welcoming smell of late-night pizza and early morning secrets but I find it hard to go in. The students who tend the bar for lodging glare suspiciously at me but I ignore them as the smell of frying mushrooms fills the room, making my mouth water. Jeff, the Forges breakfast cook gives me a welcoming wink.

'Bacon sarnie?' he offers as he tends the griddle.

I nod, feeling the cosy-covered teapot for warmth before pouring a mug and scraping a chair to the farthest corner of the table, away from the unnerving tang of the iron griddle. Away from questioning eyes. Away from Nick's accusing gaze where I can huddle in my travel-stained hoodie in peace.

'You're back then, I see,' says Jeff as he passes me breakfast. The bacon is hot and bubbling.

'Yeah,' I mutter around my first bite. The crispy fat burns my tongue but I don't stop eating. Just gulp a mouthful of the bitter black brew for some relief.

An angry snap of the newspaper echoes from the far side of the table. I ignore it.

'You were serving last night,' one of the young students calls over to me. 'Who are you, and where'd you come from all of a sudden?'

'I'm old staff,' I mumble around a claggy mouthful of bread. It's not a lie. I've spent many years working here, just not the last one.

'But,'

'Lisa, drop it,' Jeff warns her.

'But?'

'Isn't the university bus due?'

The ladle clinks against a plate as Jeff serves up breakfasts for guests in the customer dining room next door. I feel him glare at Lisa, although I keep my eyes down, staring into the depths of my mug as she and the other students reluctantly take the hint and clatter past me. Jeff manages to catch my eye and he grins reassurance as he too leaves. Leaves me alone in the kitchen, with Nick, the Forges landlord and owner.

The tap drips into the heavy silence.

I reach out to pour the last of the tea as Nick deliberately folds the paper, placing it on the table by his empty plate.

'So,' he asks, 'how long are you here for this time?'

I dismiss Nick's question with a sigh. 'That was it.' Tea ripples as I breathe into the mug. 'My last fling in the wider world. Iron and ink are becoming too strong for me to go anywhere anymore.'

'And Jaclyn?'

I have to look at him as a thousand answers clamber for prominence on my tongue but I can't reply honestly to his undertone of pain. I can't reply at all.

'Who?' I whisper, wincing at the sound of my indifference.

'Your travelling companion. The woman you ran off with.' Nick pauses, trying to be strong but his eyes are liquid with unshed tears, 'My wife, mother of my son.'

'Oh.' I have to get out of the room. Draining the tea, I stand up to leave. I can't lie and I certainly can't tell him the truth. I'm trapped by a wish.

'Todd, what happened?' he pleads.

I am fae, I tell myself. Why should I care what happened to one life in the suffocating multitude of humanity? I hate that I am shaking inside so I fall into old, arrogant ways.

'She died,' I say, offhand. 'You know this. Mortals have such short lives.'

Nick's voice cracks. 'Don't do this to me.'

The table is rough under my hands as I grip its edge, staring out of the kitchen window. When did we get yellow curtains? I try to ground my thoughts into human, but all I can think of are Jaclyn's pleading eyes.

'I can't lie, you know that, fae can't lie,' I tell him. But I'm going to have to learn.

'You ran off with my wife,' Nick growls.

'I didn't,' I breathe. The truth. Nor did she run off with me, although I would have happily followed her to the ends of the earth if she'd asked.

'It was an accident; I couldn't have prevented it.' I glance at Nick, chew on my thumb. The truth again. The car had come out of nowhere.

'She didn't suffer,' I mutter.

No, I'd made sure of that.

That had been the plan all along.

'How the fuck would you know what suffering looks like?' Nick slams his fists on the table making the crockery dance with his rage. 'You amoral, insensitive scrap of fairy trash.'

How well Nick knows me. I push aside the dirty plate, taking care not to touch the scattered cutlery, and sit myself on the wooden kitchen table, feeling its ancient history through my fingertips. History that was cut short due to humans and iron. I cross my legs, tucking bare feet under dirty knees, and lean forward. Looking into Nick's despairing face I let the insult fill me with anger and spite. It was always easier to deal with mortals this way.

'Your kind have taken away my magic,' I spit, 'imprisoned me in your world, where everything is tainted by iron and ink and it burns, everyday it burns and I have to live with it forever and you tell me I don't know what suffering is!'

I shake my head as I trail fingers across the table. Wood still has a purpose. I have not. How can I be fae if magic is all but gone? Sitting back with a sigh, I let the last of the glamour spell clinging to my skin, making me appear human, melt into the bacon-scented air.

'Your wife wanted to travel, you wanted to stay. I granted her wish.' Oh, how I twist the truth so I don't have to lie. 'We saw so much wonder,' I try to reassure Nick. 'Had so much fun.'

I push back the hood to let the weight of long silver hair flow down my back, scraping it into a knot so that he can see all of my strangeness, the sharp chin, cat slit violet eyes, my up-curled, pointed ears.

He catches his breath at the sight. I don't want to fight any more. I have to tell him. But I can't say what he needs to hear.

'Magic is fading out of the world but I cannot ignore the power-ful command of a last wish.' It's true but I am misleading him.

And has nothing to do with what happened to Jaclyn but the words still hurt me.

'A last wish?' Nick's voice wavers with faint hope. I nod, reaching over the teapot to cup Nick's cheek with my thin cold, alien-looking hand.

'I promised I would give her...' Teeth and tongue rebel against my words '... my last grantable wish.' This isn't true, I gave her my last grantable wish as a wedding gift seven years ago. Never imagined that she would use it, use me to end herself before she became an empty shell like her mother. Never imagined that I would have to carry the burden and the secret of her death in my heart as she couldn't bear to tell her family the truth. Never imagined that she'd use my wish to make me lie about it. I clap poison reddened lips together as the bacon sandwich threatens to come back up.

 Nick doesn't notice.

'And?' His simple hope hurts more that my burning lips.

'A wish cannot turn aside a person's destiny.'

I've led him astray as all fae do but not in a good way. He thinks I took Jaclyn away because she wanted to travel. I took her away to die. And my poison coated lips did the deed.

'I'll be in tonight to help on the bar,' I mumble, trying to act normal as the lie takes its toll. I am being punished but I can't die of my own poison. Only squirm in pain as I rush out of the door and curl up into a heap of shivering agony.

I have fulfilled Jaclyn's last wish. I have not told her loved ones that she had the same disease that took away her mother. That her childhood fear stopped her from speaking about it once the doctor had confirmed it a year ago. That I killed her, cleanly rather than the slow brain death she feared.

Now I have come home.

Being a Horse
Lizzi Linklater

over scorched plains we stampede tethered by herd threaded by scent wind
hot salty whips our manes tumbles them coarse drenched by storms green
grasses blaze hooves dust up soil happy under sharp skies beating tattoo of
sun giddy we are with the rushby our eyes liquid propelled forward trees
shaped strange watchful mountain peaks rivals heed our path the smell
of them strong at rest we nuzzle sigh prance tails high if we hurt oh the
shivering and shrugging tail slapping groaning unquiet in our misery
jumpy in our joy

I have cantered
rocky terrain
gut driven,
steered by senses.
A sweep of the head enough to scrutinise,
taste truth's tang, scent out the spice of lies.
Restless as weather, I have moved fast,
even on legs lamed and pained.
Defiant despite blizzard or squall.
My kind are finely tuned.
Rich with resonating chords; our harmony precarious.
We slip into discordance, hypersensitive
to the resounding gong, the clanging cymbal.

The consultant says my immune system is broken.
He is not to know my condition fits that of the aging equine.
I do not tell him that my sort share what he outlines:
a supersensitive fight-flight response,
strong neural reactions of the hypothalamus,
consequential activation of the pituitary, secretions
of hormones, release of adrenaline: a gloopy gush of cortisol,
suppression of the immune system leading, like a hated harness,
to damage of muscle, brain, organ and bone. And a blasting fatigue
that slams
us to shiver, our strings sundered.

I have hidden myself within my herd they groom me nuzzle my neck
whinny sing songs of solace nudge me to greener pastures comfort my
sorrowed heart snort stamp hard the earth at my sick scent restless they
are to sprint light footed yet in this darkest of valleys their liquid eyes kiss
me as they bide sunrise to moonrise rain and shine watchful wary waiting

Shroud
Lizzi Linklater

After From the Lake No. 1 by *Georgia O' Keeffe*
1924, Lake George, New York, USA

Wrap me in this painting.
Copy it onto a fine muslin,
enough to drape me.

Carry me out. The lake will cover
me: head, face, limbs, torso,
all of me swaddled tight.

Match my brow to the sapphire storm,
skull to the restless clouds, and be sure
my fingers touch the sun's acid light.

Clothe my stomach in turquoise
waves, breasts in white spiked swell,
neck cyan, legs brushed lime.

You know how my head gets.
How it feels slammed, crashed as if against
bricks. How I need tides to tame me.

Remember to cushion my feet. Fit azure,
mint, grass and olive to my soles.
You know I'll need to dance.

Organise a blast of oceanic singing
then transport me sheathed sleek
to the muted, muffled earth.

Don't fret, love. In the rumbling soil, waves
will caress me as my decomposing flesh mingles
paint, water, swell and the soft kiss of cloth.

Fold me in the painting. After it's done
watch closely. See the aqua earth ripple, billow,
rush and rise. That will be me, dancing.

Bear and the Ice
Martin Watts

Bear with her friends Beaver and Tansy all worked in the Museum Gardens. They planted the plants, weeded the weeds and kept things tidy. It was autumn, and they were playing with the leaves.

'Gotcha!' hissed an Important Person. 'You shouldn't be playing with leaves, you should be raking them up!' The Important People were in charge and told everyone what to do.

A flood of water nearby had frozen solid. Children were larking, slipping, sliding and some were even skating on it.

'You're not supposed to have fun!' the Important Person ordered. 'Also, I don't want everyone, especially children, playing on this ice, it must go. It's a pernicious puddle, a dangerous drainage malfunction, an icy irritation. We need the gardens tidy for the arrival of our Famous Guest from Russia, so hurry up!' and he marched off.

Bear went to the edge of the ice. It was hard and the colour of milky tea. Skating can't be that difficult, she thought. She stepped onto the ice and stood swaying forwards and backwards, wobbled and fell with a terrific crash. Oh dear, skating was a bit tricky.

'What you need,' said Tansy Beetle as she picked up Bear's spectacles and polished them, 'is a partner and then you can hold each other up. That's what all the great skaters do.'

'Oh yes,' said Beaver brushing bits of ice from Bear, 'I had a Canadian Uncle who was a champion skater and his partner was a Delicate Elk.'

Bear wondered who she could ask to be her partner. After all, she didn't know any Delicate Elks.

She watched the children larking on the ice.

'What are they doing?' said a voice next to her. Bear looked down. There was a very thin old lady.

'Larking,' said Bear, 'having fun, sliding and skating.'

'I used to be quite good at skating,' smiled the old lady, 'I haven't done much lately, my hands and feet get so cold.'

'Here, take my arm,' said Bear and she tucked the old lady's cold fingers into her fur.

'Oh, what a wonderful fur coat,' said the old lady.

'It's not a fur coat,' said Tansy Beetle, 'it's Bear.'

'Oh, I do beg your pardon,' said the old lady, 'but it is lovely and warm.'

'It keeps me warm when it's cold enough to freeze the floods,' laughed Bear.

'Skating was such fun,' mused the old lady, 'but I shan't be doing it anymore.'

'Why not?' asked Bear.

'Oh, I can still skate, you never forget, but I can't see very well,' said the old lady. 'I would need someone to take the lead.'

'Ah,' wondered Bear, and she looked very closely at the old lady.

'I wonder,' she said, 'if you wouldn't mind being my Delicate Elk?'

'Your what?' said the old lady.

'I mean, could you hold me up?'

'Hold you up?'

'No, I mean be my partner, my skating partner.'

'Can you skate?' asked the old lady.

'Well,' said Bear, 'bears are very familiar with the snowy wastes and icy mountains.'

'Can you skate?' asked the old lady.

'Some bears live on snow all the year and sleep in ice caves at minus a hundred degrees.'

'Can you skate?' snapped the old lady, and she stamped her foot.

'Almost I can, well, not all the time. To tell the truth,' sighed Bear,' not really.'

'Oh, I see,' said the old lady. 'That's good. I shan't have to correct your bad habits!'

So, they stepped out hand in paw onto the ice. Bear guided the old lady, the old lady held Bear, whispering instructions. 'Push and glide and push and glide, now turn.'

They skated slowly around until Bear's legs felt quite wobbly.

'Thank you so much,' said Bear out of breath, 'you're a wonderful teacher.'

'Not at all, 'said the old lady. 'Thank you for bringing back happy memories.'

The next morning the friends were having a quick cuppa before starting work. An Important Person was striding towards them. 'Looks like trouble,' said Bear.

'We're going to be for it,' said Beaver.

'You can always tell when they're bursting to shout at you,' said Tansy Beetle.

'What are you doing?' shouted the Important Person.

'Told you', said Tansy Beetle.

The Important Person continued to shout, 'We still have this pernicious puddle, this dangerous drainage malfunction, this icy irritation. Break all the ice up! Clear it away! Our Famous Guest is due any minute and I don't want them slipping over or seeing all these horrid children larking about.'

Suddenly there was a great fanfare and everyone was running to the main entrance to see the Famous Guest.

'Oh, it's too late,' said the Important Person and they dashed off. The three friends quickly swept a pile of leaves over the ice to hide it.

The Famous Guest and the Important People began their tour of the gardens. 'Take me to your skating pool,' said the Famous Guest.

'We don't have one,' said the Most Important Person.

'You had one yesterday. I had a wonderful time skating with a Bear.'

'You must be mistaken.'

'Mistaken!' retorted the Famous Guest and she stamped her foot on the edge of the pile of leaves and began to slip. Bear, quick as a flash, grabbed her arm and held her up.

'Oh, it's my skating partner,' she said. 'I recognise your wonderful fur. Shall we skate?'

As quickly as they could, Tansy Beetle, Beaver and some of the children, rushed in to clear away the leaves making the ice ready for the skaters.

So, Bear took the hand of Countess Irina Petrovna Danceofskaia, the famous Russian Olympic skating champion, and together they stepped onto the ice.

Bear waved at her friends.

'Concentrate,' said the Countess.

Starting slowly the great Bear and the Countess began to skate.

'She's like the Delicate Elk,' smiled Beaver.

'They hold each other up,' laughed Tansy Beetle. ,

'Let's go faster,' whispered the Countess into Bear's furry black ear. So round and round they went, faster and faster. 'And twirl!' she cried, and all the rest of the leaves went up in a great whoosh. Everyone cheered and clapped.

'Such fun,' she laughed,' to play in the leaves and skate.'

Everyone stepped on to the ice and skidded and skated, slipped and larked. Everyone, that is, but the Important People, who stood on the edge and scowled.

Genetic Sequence
Griselda Goldsbrough

Genome editing

   Where   Change, cut, remove, add, replace,
Is   edit single, multiple genes.
  The   Observe, change human health.
     Self?

Embryos

Human genome editing   leap.
largely forbidden; surviving
between the documentation policies.
Where the legal landscape labels
countries restrictive, permissive or
something in-between.
Removal of CCR5 gene allowed
the first controversial

It's Not Me, It's You

You	Genomes are complicated.
Influence	Your traits are controlled,
How	on top of that
Your	the way you live, your choices,
Genome	you smoke, you drink, you don't sleep enough.
Works	It's not your destiny.

100,000 Genomes

ATCG   Whole genome sequencing
   TCGA   looks at every letter of DNA
CGAT   to find the change
    GATC   responsible for the rare diseases
 ATCG   that are difficult to diagnose.
     TAGC   It identifies a condition
    AGCT   that initiates treatment
GCTA   shares answers
      GCAT   support and expertise
        TGCA   gives a transformational gift.

Intensive Care
Polly Gibson

Metal u bends, hanging curtains, cleaners wiping floors.
Hands held. Eyes avoiding.
Ice in muslin,
cold against the lips.

Machines, machines, machines.
Hard machines, breathing tubes.
No voice. No sunlight.
Chilled dead air.

Whoosh – whoosh – whoosh
Up – down - up – down
Whoosh – whoosh – whoosh
Drip – drop – drip
Drop.
Ice in muslin, cold against her lips.

Searching for a Miracle
Polly Gibson

I need a charm to hold
against the night sky.
To shine light through the whispers
of incantations
of prayers
of wishes
of desires.
I need a charm that fulfils promises
beyond smiling horseshoes, touching wood,
fingers crossed.
Beyond the rabbit's foot, four leaf clover
and salt, thrown.
I need a charm that answers hope.
A candle to forever shine bright.
I need a miracle.

At Last
Polly Gibson

At Last

we lay

s t r e t c h e d

in bed.

Hospital sheets and hangman drip

taken for another.

Our skin touches – her fingers – in mine.

I kiss – her – bruises – stroke her skin

whisper – baby – home –

at last.

The Problem
Graham Kennedy

Connor had his hands spread apart holding the sides of his bathroom sink. He gazed at his reflection in the mirror.

'You're in my head. You're completely in my head and I can't get you out of there. Jesus! What am I going to do? I'm completely fucked.'

He turned on the tap, splashed some water on his face and ran his hands through his hair. He went out of the bathroom, sat down on his lounge chair and faced his best friend.

Rocco stared at him. 'You look a mess, mate.'

'I am a mess.' Connor rubbed his forehead with his fingertips as if he was trying to massage his brain.

He suddenly stopped and locked eyes with Rocco. 'I don't think I can go through with the wedding.'

'Look, I'm your best mate and anything you decide...I'll support you, but I'm also your best man and I'd just like to say that I've spent a lot of money on that blue suit you chose, and I've bought you a really expensive present. My names Rocco not Rockefeller.'

Connor saw the big grin on Rocco's face. They both started laughing. 'You're a complete dick sometimes.'

'I know, but you're a bigger one and that's why I like you…It's not the end of the world but you hardly know this girl.'

'You get to know someone quickly when nutters are trying to kill you…She saved me. I wouldn't be here if it wasn't for her.'

'Yeah, I know all that, but that doesn't mean she's the right girl for you, whereas you've been going out with Miss World for five years. She's always been the one. Everyone adores her.'

Connor stood up and started pacing around the room. 'I feel so guilty. Lottie doesn't deserve this. I hate myself.' He looked directly at his friend and stopped walking. 'Do you remember that day when we were at the table before all the shooting, and you asked me why I looked so glum? It was because I had doubts in my head then.'

'What doubts?'

'It was as if all this happened for a reason.'

'Oh, come on. Get real. Do you think Johnny Terrorist and all those crazy fuckers started killing everyone because you didn't invite them to your wedding? I didn't read that in the Sunday Times. I thought it was because they were all fucking mental.'

'Very funny. You should be on a stage.' He paused, 'there's another reason.'

'What other reason? Don't tell me you've found God and want to be a priest?

'I had sex with her.'

'You what! Are you crazy? Jesus, what did you do that for? Now you're screwing up two women's lives. You're engaged to be married in five weeks.'

'I didn't mean it to happen. It just did.'

'Oh yeah. How did it ... just happen?'

'I arranged to meet her at Richmond Park, and we went for a walk. I couldn't take my eyes off her. There's something fantastic about her. She's so different to me and she makes me laugh. She's clever and she's got nerves of steel. She could've run off, but she came back and shot that nutter. We have that bond. Something special happened that day.'

'God, you didn't have sex in the park, did you? It's lucky you weren't arrested. That would be brilliant. I can see the head-line now: "Hero and heroine of massacre caught fornicating in park!" Your parents would love that. So how did it happen?'

'We came out the park and I walked her to my car and said I would give her a lift to the tube. She sat in the passenger seat and I was just staring at her, saying nothing. Her eyes are emerald green. They're mesmerising. Before I knew what I was doing, I reached over and kissed her. She didn't resist; it was electric. It was like someone had turned on a switch in both of us. I had her blouse off in seconds and then she said, 'In the back.' She jumped in between the seats, and I followed. The windows are blacked out and I put my jacket over the seats to sort of cover us. She was crazy. It was the best sex I've ever had in my life. It was mental and I loved it. So did she. It was so risky and spontaneous. Lottie would never have done that. There was even a guy who walked by with his dog, but she just laughed.

She's wild and I loved it. I just can't get her out of my head.'

'Jesus, Connor. It's only sex. We did that when we were teenagers. You're thirty-one. You're meant to have affairs after you're married not five weeks before your honeymoon.'

'I can't go through with the wedding. I've betrayed Lottie. I feel such a shit. But it can't be right. Can it? I thought I loved Lottie, but now I don't know. I've done something really wrong. I won't be able to look her in the eye. She'll see right through me. She always does.' He looked long and hard at his friend. 'Anyway, it was time you bought yourself a decent suit.'

Did you tell Pussy Galore that you were engaged to be married?'

'Her name's Cara, but yes I told her I was engaged, but I didn't tell her that I'm meant to be getting married in five weeks. She feels guilty too, but we couldn't help ourselves. She says it's weird as she knew something special happened when our eyes first met.'

'But do you really want to give up a beauty like Lottie for a girl you hardly know, just because you had amazing sex in the back of a car? My advice is to get married, have a kid and then have an affair with your secretary, just like everyone else.'

'You're no help at all. It's not like that. Even before the attack when I saw her in the bar, I felt drawn to her. Like I said, I think fate brought us together.'

Rocco picked up his phone. 'Hold on a second.'

'What are you doing?'

'I'm checking Instagram.'

'Why?'

'I'm seeing if the guy with the dog caught you on camera. It'll be great for the stag do.'

'God, Rocco, sometimes you are such a wanker. You're my best friend. I need some help here.'

'What do want me to say? I don't know the girl. None of us do. I've only seen her photo in the papers and sure … she's a stunner, but so's Lottie and you're going to break her heart… Do you really want to do that? Think of the repercussions.'

'I just can't go through with it. I'd be living a lie. My dad says, face your demons or they'll consume you.'

'Have you told your parents?'

'God no. They both adore Lottie. They'd think I'm mad.'

'Well, that's the first demon you'll have to face and it won't be the last.'

'I know… I'm screwed.'

'Ok. I've an idea. Why don't you postpone the wedding? Say you have PTSD. It's probably not far from the truth. There were eight people killed that day and fifteen wounded. One of them could have easily been you. It's a get out of jail free card. I guess that Lottie's dad might murder you anyway if you tell him you're ditching his golden girl because she doesn't like sex in the back of a car in broad daylight.'

'It's not just about the sex, Rocco.'

'Oh yeah?'

Connor's phone rang on the table. They both glanced at the caller ID. It was Lottie.

Haibun
Jools Lambert

A Nostalgic Trip

Found eventually down a leafy road in the suburbs. A place
we both worked in decades past. The modern sign shocks.
Bold, garish hues greet us.

The orchard where I sat to enjoy the sun now a car park. The
ward I worked in now a museum. We enter a space recently
transformed. Bright and airy, a model of today's fashionable,
primary colours. Oak seats to sit on and enjoy modern paintings. Also, grainy black and white images of former patients.
Among them artists and writers long dead.

Commentary on treatments once prescribed. Judged and
condemned long since.

Other pictures capture our own time there. Reminders of
uniforms long abandoned. Starched collars and aprons. Six-
ties hairstyles tucked under white linen hats.

We reminisce and reluctantly agree.
We too are a part of history.

a Beatles soundtrack
for our road trip
to Bedlam

Solstice Spiral

We leave the lodge at 7.45 am. Step on to a path frosted
overnight so tread cautiously. It's still dark; the sun won't be
up for another hour. The main hall is silent as we enter and
join the group of people already gathered. Here to dance the
Solstice spiral into a green reality.

A recorder and hoop drum hold a gentle rhythm. The
circle joins hands and we dance the spiral template. As the
music fades into the final notes, we stand in a circle of deep
silence.

Gardeners arrive with wheelbarrows of ever-greens newly
cut. Spruce, holly, ivy and yew. Nature's offerings for our
evening celebration. Willing hands work quietly. The bright-
ness of red and white berries fleck the different hues of
greenery as our spiral grows.

At day's end the community will gather in meditation. Walk
the spiral by candle light to celebrate the Earth's turning. We
will bring our own inner stories to share. Offer gratitude for
the return of the light and the blessings it will bring.

as ancients once did
we walk the green path
in silence

El Caballo
Lizzi Linklater

Anarchic. A helter-skelter of a beast.
Hangs round el granjero's herd,
flips his vast frame this way and that.

On the dusty field he nuzzles amigos.
Hurls - spine first - to the sandy earth;
hefty hooves play the air like a harp.

And here's el granjero to trail his horses
home, his frayed ropes dangle, braided
with sweat. Beneath the pines, cloaked

by woody trunks, el caballo stands back.
Fickle, flighty, his huge neck trembles as el río
rushes, hushes. He waits for the earth to calm.

Up the cobbled street they trot, the evening
sun their halo. Niños ride majestic,
their greetings loud: ¡Señor! ¡Señora!

Abandoned, el caballo charges. Reckless
in his lonely bowl he kicks the thirsty ground,
rears thunderous. A frenzied, rowdy beast.

Canters up a choking dust cloud, speeds
to gallop, ferocious in his orbit. Steadily
slows, stops. Stomps. Bends for gulps

of rivery rainfall. Sighs. Snorts. Shakes
the blistering day from his mane. Quietened.
Stilled. He slips away to find the moon.

Notes on Spanish translations:
El Caballo — The Horse
el granjero - the farmer
amigos -friends
el río — the river
niños — children.

Sensations from a Roof Terrace
Lizzi Linklater

Even the cicadas take breaks.
A cockerel flags, a horse sighs.
Ponderous trees slump.

On the baked mountain road, a slack
bus honks, motorbikes whine, heat hangs,
mutters. Siesta slumbers...A miniscule

change breaks the swelter, breezes stir,
that fiery sun pulls back. The tempo shifts.
In seconds energy unzips as neighbours

tumble out, resume their chatter,
laughing niños scamper winding alleys,
the shutters of la tienda crash open.

Up cranks the school band; drumbeats topple,
trumpets blunder, a gusty violin swerves.
Demented as the summer storms

this cacophony swells. It kisses mountains,
wraps houses, bounces, bellows, booms,
orchestrates a solid sonic mantle.

On the opposite terrace Javier sits,
smokes; listens to the changing sky.
Not a drop of sweat on him.

Notes on Spanish translations:
niños – children.
la tienda – the shop

Fallout: A Radio Play
David Kennard

CHARACTERS
AMY: 14
MIKE: Amy's dad, garage mechanic
NINA: Amy's aunt, works for an estate agent
PAUL: Nina's husband, office manager

ACT 1.

SCENE 1.

EXT. A SUBURBAN STREET. 8.30AM

F/X: Footsteps running up a street, bus
doors opening, getting on a bus.

DRIVER: Just made it.
AMY: (Panting) Thanks.

F/X: Bus doors closing, bus driving off. AMY
flops into a seat and presses numbers on her
mobile phone. Ringing tone.

NINA: Hello.
AMY: (CLOSE) Can I come to yours tonight?
NINA: Amy? Where are you?
AMY: (CLOSE) I'm on the bus
NINA: What's happened?
AMY: (CLOSE) Dad was shouting at me
               this morning.
NINA: What?

AMY:	(CLOSE) He was really shouting at me.
NINA:	What about?
AMY:	(CLOSE) I don't know. All sorts.
NINA:	What was he saying?
AMY:	(CLOSE) Not to come back.
NINA:	What?
AMY:	(CLOSE) After school, not to come back after school.
NINA:	Oh, Amy, I'm sure he didn't mean it.
AMY:	(CLOSE) I don't want to go back.
NINA:	I need to talk to him.
AMY:	(CLOSE) Can I come?
NINA:	He has to agree. He needs to know where you are.
AMY:	(CLOSE) He doesn't care.
NINA:	He does, Amy, I'm sure he does. Look, I'll pop round and see him in my lunch break. I'm sure he didn't mean it. It's just, things are difficult for both of you at the moment. I'm going to talk to him, okay?
AMY:	(CLOSE) But I don't- Got to go!
NINA:	I'll be in touch.
AMY:	(CLOSE) Love you.
NINA:	Yeah, you too.

SCENE 2.

INT. MIKE'S LIVING ROOM. MIDDAY

F/X: Daytime TV in background.

NINA:	Mike? Door was open. Thought I'd call round, see how things are. I brought some flowers.
MIKE:	Hmm. Thanks.
NINA:	I'll go and put them in the sink.

F/X: Running water in a sink.

NINA: (OFF) Amy phoned this morning. On
                 the way to school.
MIKE: (GRUNTS AN INDISTINCT RESPONSE)

F/X: Water stops.

NINA: (OFF) Sounds like you had words.
MIKE: What she been saying?
NINA: (OFF) You didn't want her to come
                 home? After school?
MIKE: Grassing on me, eh.
NINA: Mike, you can't say that kind of
                 thing. Even if you are angry.
                 You're her dad.
MIKE: Yeah, well you weren't there.
                 It's not the same for you.
NINA: (Sighs) I know it's really
                 difficult. I miss her too you know.
                 All the time. Mind if I turn that
                 off?

F/X: Background TV stops.

MIKE: Yeah.
NINA: And Amy's not easy. And she's
                 fourteen.
MIKE: Yeah.

**F/X: Cap being prised off bottle, beer
pouring into glass.**

MIKE: Want one?
NINA: No thanks, I'm driving and I've
                 got viewings this afternoon. Why
                 she was phoning was she wanted to
                 come to ours tonight. I told her

	I'd talk to you.
MIKE:	Oh, I know what you think. She'd be better off with you and Paul now.
NINA:	It's not like that. It's just. (BEAT) If it helps to take the pressure off. I don't want to see Amy upset like this, not after all she's been through.
MIKE:	Right.
NINA:	And you, I know. Both of you. I don't think you meant it, did you. Look, why don't you message her. Tell her you're sorry. I think it's better if she's at home.
MIKE:	Yeah.
NINA:	Do something together? Watch a movie or something. Maybe you both need to make an effort. I'll tell her we've had a chat and you're going to contact her, okay? I've got to go. (BEAT) It's been good to see you, Mike. Don't forget the flowers.

SCENE 3.

INT. MIKE'S HOUSE. EVENING

F/X: Door opens. Background TV dialogue. Footsteps running upstairs.

| **AMY:** | I HATE YOU!! |
| **MIKE:** | (OFF) Amy!! For Chrissake!! |

F/X: Door slams. Sobbing. Slow fade.

SCENE 4.

INT. NINA'S KITCHEN. AFTERNOON

F/X: Door opens.

NINA:	Hi Amy, come in.
AMY:	Is Lisa here?
NINA:	She's having her tea at Maisie's, her new best friend, and Jack's at football so I'm afraid you've just got us. Hang your things over there, I'm just getting the tea ready. Paul, move over.

F/X: Door closes. Chair scrapes.

PAUL:	Hi Amy, how you doing?
AMY:	Good.
NINA:	(OFF) How were things in school?
AMY:	Okay.
PAUL:	Your dad needs a bit of sense knocked into him if you ask me, going on like that. It's not right. Should get himself back to work.
AMY:	Dad said he's been signed off with depression.
NINA:	(OFF) So why was he shouting at you? I thought you were both going to try and make an effort. . .
AMY:	We did. Dad got a takeaway and we watched this film. Then he started drinking and started going on about things, blaming me for what happened and how I was stressing him out, and I got upset and I said I didn't want to be there and he said you don't have to be.
NINA:	Oh, Amy, he shouldn't do that.
PAUL:	He shouldn't be drinking, not

	with you there.
AMY:	(PAUSE) Do you think maybe, maybe I could stay with you for a bit?
PAUL:	'course you can. Might make the idiot see sense.
NINA:	It's not that simple. She'd have to share with Lisa, you can imagine what that'd be like. It's not that we don't want you, Amy. Thing is, he is your dad. He loves you deep down.
AMY:	Funny way of showing it.
PAUL:	Let the kid stay. Give them both a break.
NINA:	I don't want him to start blaming us for taking you away.
AMY:	I think he already does.
NINA:	(Sighs) So, if we say yes, what you going to tell him?
AMY:	Do I have to tell him anything?
NINA:	You'll need to go back and get your things.
AMY:	He'll start shouting at me.
NINA:	Not if I'm there he won't.
PAUL:	Want me to come?
NINA:	No, it's okay.

SCENE 5.

INT. MIKE'S LIVING ROOM. EVENING.

NINA:	Mike, I've brought Amy back to get a few things.
MIKE:	What d'you mean?
NINA:	She wants to stay at ours for a bit. I know what I said but I think/
AMY:	give us both a break/
NINA:	for a few days.
MIKE:	You taking over then?

NINA: Amy, go and get your things.

F/X: Footsteps leaving.

NINA: I know what you think. But I'm just thinking of Amy.

MIKE: Oh yeah, that's all you do, you and Paul.

NINA: It's just for now, okay?

MIKE: She's all I've got.

NINA: So, don't drive her away, saying those things to her.

MIKE: You're not here, are you? She won't *do* anything, on her phone all the time. I have to do everything. If I say anything she flies off the handle, says she doesn't want to be here.

NINA: She's missing her mum, isn't she? Look, I know it's been really hard. I think a break will be good for both of you. Maybe you should see someone? You know, get some help.

MIKE: What's it to you? You've got what you want.

NINA: Oh, for heaven's sake, Mike! I'm doing this for all of us. Amy wants to come back, but not while it's like this.

MIKE: So, what am I supposed to do? Might as well top myself.

NINA: Don't be so fucking stupid! Amy would never forgive you, neither would I! She's already lost one parent.

MIKE: You don't understand!

NINA: I understand what it's like to lose a sister.
LONGISH PAUSE

MIKE: How long are you going to keep her?

85

NINA: Till she's ready to come back? I
               don't know, Mike, I don't know.
               We'll sort it.

F/X: Footsteps enter.

AMY: Ready.
NINA: That was quick. Okay, Mike,
               you've got my number, yeah? I'll
               get Amy to call you. Amy, you
               want to say goodbye?
AMY: (BEAT) Bye, Dad.
MIKE: (PAUSE) Be a good girl.
NINA: Come on, then.

F/X: Car doors shutting, engine starting,
car driving off.

SCENE 6.

EXT. A GARDEN. AFTERNOON

F/X: Birds singing.

PAUL: Go on, run for it. You need the
               exercise, get you off your phone.

F/X: Ball being caught.

PAUL: Okay, throw it to me.
AMY: I can't use it anyway, the
               battery's dead.

F/X: Ball being caught.

PAUL: What do you do on it all evening?
               Go on, catch!

F/X: Footsteps running, ball being caught.

AMY: (Panting) Talk to my friends.
PAUL: That's it. Brilliant. Back to
            me. How many friends you got on
            Facebook? Right, let's kick now.

F/X: **Ball being kicked.**

AMY: Nobody uses Facebook.
PAUL: What do they use? Come on, get
            those legs moving!

F/X: **Footsteps running, ball being kicked.**

AMY: (Panting) Instagram.
PAUL: On Instagram then.

F/X: **Ball being kicked.**

AMY: I don't know. Couple of hundred?
PAUL: And at school? How many friends
            have you got?

F/X: **Ball bounces a few times on the ground.**

AMY: They all hate me.
PAUL: What do you mean?
AMY: They've all stopped talking to
            me.
PAUL: Why?
AMY: I don't know. Since Mum died.
PAUL: Do you think maybe you stopped
            talking to them?
AMY: Maybe.
PAUL: Fancy a cup of tea? Come on.

SCENE 7.

INT. NINA'S KITCHEN. AFTERNOON.

F/X: **Door opening. Feet tramping in.**

PAUL: Better put that phone away, Nina, I'm trying to set Amy a better example. We've been doing a spot of training.

F/X: AMY collapses onto a chair.

AMY: (Breathing heavily) I'm exhausted.

NINA: I'm looking up some recipes I could show Amy. There's an easy one here for lasagne.

AMY: I'm useless at cooking.

PAUL: Maybe time to start learning.

NINA: (TO PAUL) You're a fine one to talk. You can start by putting the kettle on if you're making a cuppa.

F/X: Kettle filling with water.

PAUL: We'll try you in the football team next week.

AMY: No thanks.

NINA: So, do you help at all at home?

AMY: Not really.

NINA: Do you think maybe you could? A bit more now?

AMY: Don't really have time.

NINA: Really?

AMY: Homework. Doing my hair and my nails. Chatting with friends. Hollyoaks. All takes time.

NINA: You don't spend time with your dad?

AMY: Not really. He's always on at me to do stuff so I try and keep out of his way.

NINA: What sort of stuff?

AMY: I don't know. Cleaning my room.

	Putting clothes away. Cleaning the bathroom. Washing up. Just loads.
NINA:	Sounds reasonable to me. I expect Jack and Lisa to do the same. Sometimes I have to shout at them.
PAUL:	(OFF) She does.
NINA:	And at you. By the way what time are those two due back?
PAUL:	(OFF) About half an hour.
NINA:	Is that the time! I'd better get the tea on.
PAUL:	Why don't you get Amy to help you. After she's had a cuppa.
NINA:	Good idea.
AMY:	Really? OK.

SCENE 8.

EXT. A GARDEN. EARLY MORNING.

F/X: Birdsong. Fade. Footsteps on udergrowth.

NINA:	There you are. I wondered where you'd got to. Lisa said you slipped out while she was still in bed. It's chilly, are you warm enough?
AMY:	I'm all right. I like it here.
NINA:	It's a bit of the garden we never got round to clearing. Need to watch out for those brambles.
AMY:	I know.
NINA:	That log makes a good seat. Move up.

F/X: Feet crackling on twigs.

NINA: Oh, look at that.
AMY: It's a red admiral.
NINA: Oh, well done. Your mum used to
            love butterflies. She was a bit of
            a butterfly herself.
AMY: I know.
NINA: A day doesn't go by I don't think
            about her.
AMY: Me too.
NINA: Yeah. Come here.

F/X: NINA pulls AMY toward her and hugs her.

AMY: Do you think she can see us?
NINA: I'm sure she can. She's probably
            up there thinking what's Amy
            doing in Nina's garden this early
            in just her PJs?
            <u>AMY GIGGLES.</u>
            She loved you very much. Never
            forget that.
AMY: Sometimes I was afraid she was
            going to leave when they had
            big rows and she said Dad was
            stressing her out and everything
            was stressing her out.
NINA: I know. She used to phone me.
            We'd talk for hours sometimes.
            She'd never have left you, it's
            just how she was. Sometimes I
            think she and Mike were so...like
            she married someone who was the
            opposite of how she was. What's
            the opposite of a butterfly?
AMY: I think Dad's like a hedgehog,
            soft on the inside and spikey on
            the outside.
NINA: That's good, I like it. Do you
            think he'll be soft or spikey
            when you go home?
AMY: I don't know.

NINA:	When did you last talk to him?
AMY:	Last Sunday.
NINA:	How was he?
AMY:	Okay.
NINA:	Didn't you tell me he said he was starting back at work?
AMY:	Yeah, he did.
NINA:	Why don't you give him a ring this evening? Tell him what you've been up to. See how things are.

SCENE 9.

INT. AMY'S BEDROOM. EVENING

F/X: Ringtone for a few seconds.

MIKE:	Hello.
AMY:	Hi Dad.
MIKE:	Hi Amy, how's it going?
AMY:	Okay. Good.
MIKE:	They been alright?
AMY:	Yeah. Great. Uncle Paul's a bit of a pain.
MIKE:	Yeah.
AMY:	Says I don't do enough exercise, on about joining Lisa's football team.
MIKE:	How's it going with Lisa?
AMY:	She lets me use her iPad, but she can be a cow sometimes like when I'm trying to listen to my music. Can I have an iPad?
MIKE:	We'll see. And don't call people cows.
AMY:	(BEAT) Did you go back to work?
MIKE:	Yeah, back at the garage this week.
AMY:	Was it okay?
MIKE:	A load of jobs to catch up on,

	but it's better than being at home. It's been very quiet here the last couple of weeks.
AMY:	I miss you.
MIKE:	(BEAT) I miss you. PAUSE.
AMY:	Can I come home?
MIKE:	Do you want to?
AMY:	You won't shout at me?
MIKE:	No. It'll be okay.
AMY:	Promise?
MIKE:	Promise.
AMY:	(BEAT) When can I come?
MIKE:	How about Saturday?

SCENE 10.

INT. MIKE'S LIVING ROOM. MORNING

NINA:	Hi, Mike! Amy wanted me to come in first. She's in the car. She's a bit anxious.
MIKE:	What about?
NINA:	You? She hasn't seen you for two weeks.
MIKE:	We spoke on the phone. I told her it was fine.
NINA:	I know, but...Have you seen anyone?
MIKE:	What?
NINA:	Counselling.
MIKE:	Three month waiting list. I put my name down.
NINA:	Huh. You probably won't need it by the time you get an appointment.
MIKE:	How was she?
NINA:	Amy was fine. It was a bit of a job getting her off her phone but once she got the hang of talking

	to people she was okay. She and Lisa got on. I think it was good for Lisa actually, learning to think of others. So she's welcome any time.
MIKE:	Thanks. Thanks. (BEAT) It's a big adjustment.
NINA:	Maybe we could all go to the cemetery tomorrow. I can take some fresh flowers.
MIKE:	Yeah. Okay. That'd be good.
NINA:	I'll get Amy.

F/X: Footsteps. Car door opens and closes. Footsteps.

| MIKE: | You're looking well, Amy. |
| NINA: | Well, I'll love and leave you, I'm sure you've got loads to catch up on. I'll give you a ring this evening, Amy. |

F/X: Footsteps. Car door closes. Car drives off.

| MIKE: | It's good to have you back. Come here. |

F/X: MIKE gives AMY a hug.

| MIKE: | I've bought you a present. It's in your bedroom. |
| AMY: | Guess what? I've learned to cook lasagne. |

END

Tanka
Jools Lambert

two metres distance
from the crib-
only the verger
sees the tiny face mask
on baby Jesus

market stall banter
"Do those plants need watering?"
"No love, just let them die" …
market stall banter
on a bright winter day

reddened hands
reach for more sanitizer -
her mask masks
the unexpected expletive
of sting on paper cuts

the annual reunion
more silver hair than gold
as we reminisce-
also sadly acknowledge
one less place at the table

Joyful Collaborations
Graham Clift

We always went to the canteen first.

'Let's have a coffee and a chat to start with,' I'd say, 'and I'm paying. I might look old but I was a student once too.'

I would run through the basics; health and safety, hygiene, safeguarding, signing in, how the ward staff are great but don't have much time. 'Just stop me if you've got any questions.'

They always asked, 'What's it like on the ward?'

'Oh, you can feel every emotion in two hours on there,' I'd say, 'but it's good.'

'What do you say to the patients?' they wanted to know.

'It's different for everyone. Let me tell you about some patients I've known. When I was still fairly new a nurse said, "Go and talk to Moses in bed 12."'

* * *

Moses was laid flat on the bed, tubes everywhere. His face, black and shiny, was dominated by a big white plaster holding a tube in his nose.

'Hello,' I said, 'I'm a volunteer. Do you mind if I sit and have a chat with you?'

He never moved a muscle. His eyes just stared at me.

What do I do? I thought. 'Only I need your permission, you see ... 'Would you like me to sit and talk to you?'

 I crouched down so he could see me better. He just looked right into me. It was uncomfortable. Like he was seeing deep inside, weighing my soul. Then, he moved his eyes slightly to one side towards the chair. So, I took that as a 'yes' and sat down.

I waited hoping he didn't spot my nose twitch at the toilet odours.

'Well,' I said, 'it's a lovely morning. Out there. As I pedalled along the cycle path the sun was shining down through the new green leaves. On my way here. Rain tomorrow though.' I started scanning around for something to talk about. He had no pictures, cards or magazines. 'Well, it looks like they've got you nice and comfortable anyway.'

I sat there feeling silly. All the time he's scrutinising me.

I sighed. 'I've er, got my bag of books here. I can read to you if you want. Have you got any preference?'

He looked very serious, even slightly angry. Was he wondering why it was me sitting there, and not him? I imagined he could see all the injustice of the world from where he lay.

I burbled on, 'Only some people go mad for crime fiction and thrillers and won't look at anything else. Have you, er, any...?'

How can I get out of here? I thought. My sense of inadequacy increasing in weight, like the yellow bag of fluid hanging from the bed frame.

'I know,' I said, 'I'll read you a poem.' I took out the BBC anthology, *100 Favourite Poems*, 'I'll read through the index, and you just indicate if there's one you like.'

Nothing.

So, I picked one - John Masefield's *Sea Fever* - 'I must go down to the sea again…' I read it, and said, 'It's time for me to go now. I'll come and see you next week.'

He gave me the look. And I left.

* * *

Even though I'd felt stupid and embarrassed, I still went back every week. The tubes gradually came out. He got some speech back. It was very slurred, hesitant and effortful. But with drawing pictures, and breaking off to find an atlas, we eventually got that he was from Senegal and worked as a male nurse.

One week I said I'd been to a storytelling festival and heard some African stories. I told him one and he communicated, with his lop-sided smile, that he liked it.

Sometimes he was too tired to see me. Time passed, and one day he said to me,

'Hey Graham, I got story for YOU.'

'You've got your full voice back Moses!'

He told me this beautiful story about who we rely on when we are sick. He concluded with, 'and that's a story from my village in Senegal.'

Anyway, he made a full recovery, and didn't the staff know it. On my last visit he sat up in his chair in a brightly coloured shirt, buzzer in hand. He'd call for assistance and then direct the nurses, 'Morris in bed 16 has a loose dressing' or, 'Eddie needs the toilet.'

He talked to me about his recovery, from beginning to end. He recalled every detail of my visits, and described my first one in *excruciating* detail while laughing, 'He-hee. You didn't know what to do! But then,' he said, getting very serious, 'you read me that poem about the lonely sea and the sky. For a week after I could close my eyes and I was in my father's boat, smelling the ocean, seeing the clouds come and go, and imagining the wheel in my hand. And I knew then, I was alive and still had my mind.'

There were so many wonderful patients. There was a woman in her nineties who told me about Victorian music hall acts that her *grandfather* had seen and described to her: Dan Leno performing as different characters; Marie Lloyd with her perfect diction; Little Tich and his big boots. Her grandfather ran a theatre in Liverpool. Talk about living history. I'd go home and read more about them online. When she had a relapse and lost her speech, I was able to recap the stories she told me, including her happy memories of folding parachutes in the war. I read her John Gillespie Magee's *High Flight*, and we both shed a tear at the thought of him in his Spitfire sat on a carefully packed parachute flying through 'footless halls of air'.

Yes, it seems odd but don't be afraid to mention the war. I found that people retain happy memories despite any horrors they've experienced, and they're the ones they want to share. Perhaps we all do that when we're ill, sustaining ourselves with the highlights of our lives. Sit close and share with them. Some people will just list the names of their grandchildren and smile.

You'll meet some marvellous volunteers too. Find your own way to do the job; Davina sings with the patients, Edwin jokes irreverently with them, Sasha uses board games and puzzles. As long as you're communicating that's all that matters.

* * *

'Excuse me a moment. This is strange but someone else is talking to me... Sorry?'

'Hello. My name is Sue, I'm a volunteer. Would you like me to have a chat with you? You've had a stroke. I believe you used to be a hospital volunteer yourself?'

'Blllll...'

'Sorry?'

'Fer... Fer...'

'Try speaking slowly, and as loudly as you can. Breathe, and aim to OVER-ARTICU–LATE.'

'Po.... P, P.'

'I can see it's very difficult for you. You're telling me something beginning with "P."'

'Poem.'

March 2020
Polly Gibson

Winter's cold shadow

eclipses spring's sweetest breath.

Millions fallen.

Hugs
Joanne Foxton

I am built for hugs,
my hugs can't heal your world.
You have to grow your own.

I am built for hugs,
my hugs are not advice.
You may still worry when alone.

I am built for hugs,
my hugs can't fix life's wrongs.
I'll not chain your soul.

I am built for hugs.
I am not a wall.
My arms are scaffold to rely upon,
a comfort when you fall.

I am built for hugs,
I'll come when you call.
My arms around you help me
to be tall.

I am built for hugs
'cos hugs are what I need.
Please share these arms.
my hugs are free.

Good Friday
Julie Fearn

Maundy Thursday

We splash through Atlantic waves, my children and me. The cold water smacks their bellies. Shrieks fly across the sea swirls. Under the blaze of the high sun their downy arms tan. Now our bare heels scud over the spikey sand-dunes, bitter salt films our lips. We fall hungry on our picnic, breathless. Poor Charlotte lets out a cry as her newly peeled egg slips from her fingers, plops into the gritty sand.

Then I wake up, moan and tug the heavy duvet over my face. Try to drift back to the comfort of dreams but I can't. I roll over and check my clock: it's 5.57 am. Light seeps into the room. Spring will warm the earth and stir it back to life.

We were married on a dazzling spring day forty years ago. Soon after, Jason blazed into our world and everything glowed golden. I remember his shining hazel eyes, forever changing hue under the shifting light of day. Then, suddenly, I didn't know him anymore. It was like I'd smacked into a wall that he'd secretly built. That was the day my pink satin heels sank into the mud at his pagan wedding, deep in a forest, somewhere or other.

But everything changes, doesn't it? Fixing time is like catching mist.

Alexa squats quietly on the window sill. When I speak to her a blue light pulses around the cylinder to let me know she is listening. Why did he send me this robot as a present for my sixtieth? I had phoned him to ask but a recorded message told me,

'Sorry. I'm at a conference in Geneva.'

Everyone's sorry these days. Sorry for your wait, sorry for your loss, sorry you're sorry.

'Alexa can remind you to go out every day,' Jason texted after the thing arrived. 'It's important for your wellbeing.'

Is it now? Yesterday I showered, rolled my silvering hair into a French pleat and dabbed on pearlised lipstick. I pulled open the front door and took a deep breath. But an icy blast slapped me back. 'Robust coat needed,' I said, as I retreated into the cavern of my home.

But today I will go out. Very soon. Promise to self. I call my son to tell him of my plan but he's not answering right now. Never mind. Ellie's coming round to clean at 9.30 so I can tell her instead. She has a key to let herself in. 'You can't spend the rest of your life in bed,' she'll joke as she tugs at the bottom of my duvet before she hands me my morning coffee.

Ellie has cork-screwed hair twin daughters, and a kind husband who tells me creaky jokes as he scrubs my sash windows. I always laugh. When she laughs Ellie shakes her head from side to side and her black curls shimmy. Sometimes she brings her daughters round and they romp in my ramshackle garden. The skeleton of my children's swing is still there and their images turn in my mind.

Last summer Ellie's twins helped me dredge the suffocating weeds from the pond, which used to be my husband's job. And afterwards that day, in the humming August heat, we gorged on homemade lemonade and chocolate cake, dodging wasps and marvelling at the butterflies flitting across the golden Azalea bushes.

Last autumn Ellie invited me to the twins' birthday party. I was a little frightened as I was becoming rusty with people.

'What shall l wear?'

She laughed at me then, 'Your favourite dress, silly.'

So, I wore my powder-blue silk shift and kitten-heels: a mother-of the-bride outfit.

'How lovely you look,' said one of Ellie's friends, one hand flitting at her baggy linen tunic in an almost apologetic gesture. Her friend wore jeans and sneakers.

'Come and have some Prosecco.' Ellie tugged me across to the overflowing table where her guests were pouring themselves generous glasses of the frothy liquid.

One woman said, 'My yoga teacher's so hot.' They snorted and whooped.

I watched their kids running in and out of the house and garden, stuffing iced buns into their mouths, laughing and shrieking. And at the end of that day Ellie and I shovelled the crumbled left-overs into bin bags. Then I walked home sucking in the cool air that was scented from wisps of smoke curling from chimneys emitting a crisp autumn aroma.

I hear my front door open and footsteps in the hall. 'Hello!' Ellie's voice echoes up the stairs. It must be nine-thirty now.

We sit at my kitchen table after she's finished cleaning. Ellie prepares a roll-up cigarette with great precision, leaving no tobacco flecks behind.

'One of my ladies goes to Zumba classes. She says it's fun.'

I don't reply. Later, when she comes back from her smoke in the garden smelling of tobacco and spring air, Ellie leaves a flyer about the class on my coffee table. I haven't looked at it yet, or thrown it away. Tomorrow, maybe.

It's two thirty now and my mobile buzzes: it's my daughter Charlotte on the line.

'Mum, how about we Skype?'

'Lovely idea.'

And there she is, in her gleaming, capacious New York apartment, a plump nine-month-old bouncing on her lap. It's Berta my granddaughter. Berta, "the miracle" who arrived after three years of anguished IVF when they'd given up and flown across the globe to hatch a new life two years ago.

Then, that December, Charlotte broke the news to us over the phone. I had to go outside for air while my husband, with his back turned to me, stood pouring out celebratory whiskeys. It was Christmas Eve. Everything in our garden glistened under a blanket of newly fallen snow, the North Star glittered in the velvety sky. When I returned indoors, finally composed, I saw my husband sprawled across the cream sofa, a lifeless hand dangling from the edge, fingers curled. One crystal tumbler lay smashed on the hearth, the other brimming with golden liquid, stood on the coffee table with a delicate gift box by its side.

'I hear you have an Alexa?' Charlotte's voice brings me back to now.

'Yes. She's my new best friend.'

Charlotte laughs; she reminds me of her father: chocolate-coloured eyes, ever-smiling mouth.

'You know Mum,' Charlotte tells me, 'Alexa is a really great gadget.'

'Have you got one?' Suddenly I wish I hadn't said that in such a waspish-sounding way.

'Of course,' she beams. 'But how are you keeping?'

The baby shuffles on Charlotte's knee then grabs at the screen. Her hand looming towards me unfurling bud-like makes my heart balloon. An ancient longing opens up inside: I ache to nuzzle her warm neck; to blow raspberries into her soft, baby scented fold; to fly to the stars on her laughter. But I haven't even met her yet.

'You should come and stay with us, Mum. Please.'

Berta clacks a yellow plastic spoon on the granite-topped table. Charlotte giggles and grins at me then gently prises the spoon from her daughter's dimpled hand. The baby's face crumples for a moment and turns a fiery red, but then a blue Ragdoll cat leaps onto the table. Berta squeals and claps her hands together. The cat circles and waves her bushy tail over the screen, obscuring my view momentarily.

'I don't want to get in your way,' I half whisper.

Charlotte guffaws. 'You wouldn't. We have acres of space here.' She gestures to the echoey apartment.

I can hear sirens in the background of her call. I think of my last visit to her one Christmas when she lived in London: turning back against the swelling tides in the subterranean tube; running up the steps to gulp in fresh air to hail a cab that then crawled along the choked streets; the assault of honking horns as flashing ambulances screeched around traffic.

How on earth would I deal with New York I ask myself?

'Maybe when the weather improves,' I say.

I want to cry. She should live here: do sleep overs; share roast lamb Sunday lunches with me. Leave crumpled sweet wrappers on my car floor that annoy me. But she's so happy right now. I just can't say anything.

'Mum,' Charlotte says. 'I have to go now, I'm so sorry, but promise you'll ask Alexa about flights?'

I press my hand to the screen. 'I will love, I promise.' Meeting ended it reads and I click it shut.

Soon after, Jason sends a text saying, 'I've heard you're going to New York. Do you need help?' I will reply to him but need to think carefully first. And anyway, he's busy.

With hindsight his most pleasing gift to me was a Kindle on my fiftieth. The flimsy device shocked me then because I love the printed book. Ellie has even suggested, 'Maybe a book club's for you.' But I don't like going out alone or meeting strangers.

I sum up courage. 'Alexa find flights to New York.'

She tells me, 'There are two airports to choose from in New York.' I phone my son but his phone is diverted to voice mail. Again.

At 7.30 pm I snap on the TV and pour a large glass of whiskey, flump into the worn chesterfield and hug the cushion. I think of the day I tackled my husband's paintings. Carefully removing them from the walls and hauling the massive canvases into his garden studio. Laying the vibrant images on top of each other, old wool blankets placed between them, until the place was almost stacked to the ceiling. After I'd finished, I locked the door and haven't been back. I try to avoid noticing the dusty outlines where his paintings once hung. The staircase to the bedroom haunts me. When I've chosen a new colour scheme, I will hire a decorator.

I wake slathered in sweat at 5.45 am. The house is utterly silent. I dreamt of a plane circling New York, like a bird of prey. The pilot didn't know how to land it. A grey sky pressed hard against the buckling windows. Outside there was a streak of bloody-orange cleaving the horizon in two. I kept texting Charlotte but she wouldn't pick up. Then suddenly I was ripped from the dream.

Dazed I ask, 'Alexa what day is it?'

'Today is Good Friday.'

'It can't be...' I trail off because Easter is my favourite holiday. Those springtime buds, first tentative then stretching towards the warmth and light, wobbling, bursting open; shimmering in the breeze. The ancient cycle that repeats and renews. Where have I been? The idea I have been pushing away breaks out into a fully formed thought.

'Alexa!' I say.

The blue light pulses along the top of the cylinder. I cough. My voice wavers, and then I ask, 'What is loneliness?'

Alexa blinks and tells me, 'Loneliness is an unpleasant, usually complex emotional response to feelings of isolation.'

I catch my breath; tune her out for a few seconds but she's cold and relentless. 'One who feels lonely usually is lonely.'

For a split second I hate Alexa as the truth crashes down on me. I swing my legs off the sofa and rise up. 'Thank you, Alexa.'

'You're welcome, Joanna,' she replies.

I yank open the bureau to pull out a pen and pad.

'Alexa!' I fix my glasses on my nose. 'When's the next flight from Manchester to New York?'

'At which airport do you wish to land?' she asks.

'JFK, please.'

The dawn chorus is beginning outside.

'Joanna, due to a cancellation there's a seat on a flight leaving Manchester on Easter Sunday.'

'Book it!' I shout.

As Alexa floats the details out to me the morning light floods into the room. I text Jason to accept his offer of help and who knows, maybe he will join us in New York.

Author Biographies

Tina Anderson is a freelance translator. She enjoys writing her own words as a change from wrestling with other people's texts. Translation is a lonely profession, so being a member of Pen to Paper, a tight-knit and supportive group, has proved both enjoyable and challenging. Tina says the group offers its members the essential tools any aspiring writer needs.

Graham Clift worked in a variety of mostly land-based jobs before winding up with Defra who employed him to walk crops, talk to farmers and growers, and write reports. After retiring he began writing stories from his life, probably all in a civil service handbook style, until he joined the Pen to Paper group in 2010. There he was steered towards York University's creative writing courses and enjoyed encouragement from Pen to Paper members. His writing would never be the same again. He published his first memoir, *North Facing - Late Flowering* in 2021.

Margaret Evans was lured away from scientific research and teaching by the siren call of the Arts. She has attended many writing courses (including Arvon and Lizzi's!), performed at literature festivals, publishes frequently in a local magazine, won a York short story competition with a tale of murder (not related to personal experience), and dabbles in scribbling plays, poetry and YA novels. She has also exhibited and sold various pieces of art. When not busy with the above activities she still bashes balls around the tennis courts and the keyboard keys in church!

Julie Fearn is a writer living in York, born to Polish - Irish immigrant parents; she considers herself to be 'Poirish.' Before retirement, she worked mainly in Local Government both in the South and North of England. Julie cut her writing teeth on the short story format and has loved writing all her adult life but shied away from sharing it or considering publication in her working years. After studying creative writing with York University's Lifelong Learning programme, her story, The Baba Yaga Tree, was published in the University's Literature Anthology of 2015. She is currently writing a historical drama fictionalising her family's history and hopes this novel Northern Pole will be available in late 2022. Julie is addicted to cats, film and gherkins. And the odd glass of red wine.

Joanne Foxton is writer of fantastical tales (that she never quite finishes) and beer filled poems. She works full-time in hospitality catering so that she can afford more books, ale and dragons. Although she has no formal poetry training, she has performed some of her work with Say Owt, (a York based spoken work collective) and has two poems published in their anthologies. She also crochets, draws, writes micro flash fiction and makes things out of papier mâché. It's a wonder she has time to go to work. She can be found on Twitter @idledragon27

Polly Gibson has trained to work as a volunteer with medical students. She says 'meeting the young people in their very first year of medical school is an absolute joy'. She always comes away filled with enthusiasm for these future medics. If she can implant the importance of students looking after their own emotional health and seeing beyond the symptoms of a patient and family, she hopes to have made a difference. Her writing is driven from the need to explore and release mountains of terror and anxiety about the limits of our power over ill health and facing mortality.

Griselda Goldsbrough is one of the original members of the Pen to Paper group, enjoying the support and humour it brings and the style and quality of the teaching. She brings her keen interest in arts in health and science, particular genetics, into her writing of poetry and short stories. Griselda wears several hats as a community artist, including her ecotherapy creative writing position at St. Nicks, a local nature reserve.

Graham Kennedy has been writing fairly consistently since he was a teenager in Glasgow. He moved to York thirty years ago and completed a part-time MA in Creative Writing at York St John part time which enabled him to continue to run his business. He has written several plays and many short stories over the years. He writes for his own personal pleasure rather for any recognition or financial gain. He enjoys exploring the conflict and dilemmas of individuals, especially when writing dialogue. His piece in *Something Brewing* is part of a larger story about people who meet unexpectedly when situations arise out of their control or imaginations. Graham is a great believer in fate determining life, and also that every day on this planet is a gift to treasure.

David Kennard is a retired clinical psychologist and group analyst. He has always enjoyed writing and has written or co-produced five books for professionals and trainees working in mental health. After retiring he took up creative writing, enrolling on Lizzi's online Creative Writing Course at the University of York and then joining Pen to Paper. Scriptwriting particularly took his fancy so he also joined Script Yorkshire and has had short plays performed at Script Factor in York and at Page to Stage in Leeds.

Jools Lambert - fledgling writer for the past twenty years, one time nurse and into all things alternative. Finds inspiration in the poetry of Japan's great writers of haiku, and allied forms, together with daily reading of contemporary poetry. She has a tendency to read much more of the latter rather than creating it, but with the support and inspiration she finds in the Pen to Paper writing group is putting pen to paper, or fingers to keyboard, more regularly now. Age...well, as a teenager she saw the Beatles live in 1963. Yeah, Yeah, Yeah!

Lizzi Linklater loves literary pursuits. She has lectured widely in Creative Writing, most recently for the University of York, instigated local writing groups, set up her own courses, edited/published students and local writers and organised many flamboyant events. Published in Dreamcatcher, Circa Works, Lives Remembered and elsewhere, she has had her poetry set to music with the Sounds Lyrical Project. She attends The Poetry School where her work is fiercely but lovingly critiqued and, adoring a yarn, she also writes short stories

Jon Markes is a shopkeeper by trade. He co-writes a fortnightly serial 'Leeford Village', which is published by the Express and Star newspaper in the Midlands. Jon has been runner-up in two national short story competitions and has self-published an illustrated children's Christmas story book, 'Santa's Trousers'. He finds the critique of his work offered by fellow Pen to Paper writers extremely valuable. A selection of Jon's writing can be found at jonmarkes.com.

Loreta Vilkyte, an English and drama teacher by profession was born and raised in Lithuania. Her play 'An Auction of Unwanted Parents' won the first price in the national script writing competition in Lithuania in 2017. Loreta writes when she has time and when she is inspired by events that make her pick up a pen and start. Since she joined Pen to Paper, she has been a finalist in the Script Factor (York Branch) competition in 2019.

Martin Watts lives in the North Yorkshire Moors in the Esk Valley where the countryside is a great inspiration. He believes a good story should be read aloud and hopes people will enjoy reading about Bear. Other stories about Bear, her friends and their adventures are being written and, hopefully, will soon be available to share.

Acknowledgements
Lizzi Linklater

Something Brewing owes its existence to the support and efforts of many. Thank you to the writers of the Pen to Paper group featured within for their dedication and patience as the anthology went through the varied stages of publication. In particular: Margaret Evans who acted as an eagle-eyed co-editor with myself, and Jon Markes who advised on the publishing process.

In addition, I thank Jazmine Linklater from Carcanet Press who typeset and sorted out the pitfalls of publication, Aaron Kent from Broken Sleep Books who offered advice, the poet Antony Dunn whose shared experience in the publishing world proved inestimable and Roxannah Rio Linklater who created the artwork and design for covers.

I am indebted to Lendal Press and Seline Duzenli, who has shown support, encouragement and professionalism from my first approach. I am grateful also to Jamie McGarry for his enthusiasm in publishing the work of our long-standing writing group. The fact that Lendal Press is based in York, as we are, adds a special frisson to the volume.

Although our meeting place, the fabulous Brigantes Pub on Micklegate, ceased trading during the covid pandemic, it will always be cherished; its Upstairs Room a necessary balm to the chaotic wildness of our collective minds. Thanks also to Dylan George at Miller's Yard on Gillygate, and to Greg and Ails McGee at According to McGee who have previously housed us. We have now set up a new home at The Cross Keys Pub on Goodramgate and I thank them for their hospitality.

I thank the York Literature Festival and especially its directors Miles Salter (2009) and Rob O' Connor (2017) who accommodated our dazzling performances. The support and encouragement of the York Literature Festival for this publication is hugely appreciated.

A massive Thank You goes out to Zoom! Without it, social distancing would have caused the collapse both of the group and of the project.

Final thanks go to Jonathan Linklater who has endured the ongoing mechanisms of the production of this anthology with his characteristic generosity and encouragement.